The Therapeutic Management of Psychological Illness

The Therapeutic Management of Psychological Illness

THE THEORY AND PRACTICE OF SUPPORTIVE CARE

Werner M. Mendel
Gerald Allen Green

BASIC BOOKS, INC., PUBLISHERS
New York London

© 1967 by Basic Books, Inc.
Library of Congress Catalog Card Number: 67–13365
Manufactured in the United States of America
Designed by Florence D. Silverman

This book is dedicated to the memory of Franz Alexander, teacher, therapist, and humanist, whose pioneering spirit and openness to new ideas inspired us to return to the patient in our quest for a theory of treatment.

Preface

In the past fifty years medicine has made major strides in developing definitive interventions in illness and injury. As we discover the cause and subsequent cure and prevention of illness, our attention is focused on the dramatic, acute interventions. Yet all of us recognize that most of our time, attention, and energy are devoted to patients with conditions that require support, rehabilitation, and palliation. Thus, though the drama and romance of medicine have been focused on the cure and prevention of illness, the everyday work of medicine remains in the area of management of illness. That management which relieves suffering, prevents complications, and allows the patient to function at or near his capacity is the technique which we choose to call supportive care.

In psychiatry there are a number of illnesses, notably schizophrenia, for which there is no approach or method of intervention so definitive that it can be thought of as producing a cure. There are, however, methods of management that foster remission, prevent complications, and support function in the schizophrenic patient. In this book we describe techniques of care for the chronic schizophrenic patient, as well as the theoretical basis for these interventions. It is our hope that, by presenting these theoretical considerations first, we can assist the reader to apply in a more meaningful way the clinical suggestions that are discussed in the second part of the book.

The techniques described here were derived primarily from our work with chronic schizophrenic patients. They are not limited in applicability to this group of patients, however. The same techniques can be used in the management of patients with other conditions that are chronic and that cannot be basically altered. Such conditions include the borderline states, the severe character disorders, and some chronic depressive states.

This volume is written primarily for the psychiatrist, who necessarily spends a significant portion of his time in the management of patients with chronic emotional and mental disorders. Nevertheless, these techniques are not limited in usefulness only to a psychiatric practice. Although estimates vary, it is generally agreed that upward of one-half of the patients in the practices of nonpsychiatrist physicians are those who seek help for a condition that is both chronic and not significantly organic in nature. Many presenting complaints are, in fact, somatic manifestations of anxiety, and the nonpsychiatrist physician to whom the majority of such patients first address their complaints can, by sensitive and understanding use of the doctor-patient relationship, practice successful supportive care.

The treatment of the large population of chronic schizophrenic patients remains a major logistic challenge to psychiatric technique. With the simple, effective, and empirically derived techniques described in this book, many non-physician representatives of the helping situation can participate in the care of this group of patients. Psychologists, social workers, occupational therapists, nurses, ministers, and other counselors, in the proper setting and with adequate training and supervision, can also be effective supportive therapists.

As is the case with empirical methodologies, we have arrived at this approach through experience with patients. Our theoretical orientation is based on a psychoanalytic understanding of motivation with an existential view of illness and treatment emphasizing activity, reality, and structure.

University of Southern California   *Werner M. Mendel, M.D.*
School of Medicine   *Gerald Allen Green, Ph.D*
Los Angeles, California
March 1967

Contents

Part I

THEORY

1

The
Illness

————————————————————◆
————————————————————◆
————————————————————◆

Knowledge of psychiatry is based on direct observation of the behavior of human beings with themselves and with others in social settings and in isolation. From this behavior, the observer makes inferences and develops a conceptual framework that then leads to further observation and further inference. All psychiatric concepts, however, regard behavior that is bothersome either to society or to the individual as an illness. In this medical metaphor, the patient is defined as being ill; this definition has many implications in terms of the patient's responsibility for his behavior, intervention as treatment, and the kinds of interventions regarded as beneficial, ranging from chemical and surgical attack on behavior to psychotherapeutic transactions.

The assignment of diagnoses to psychiatric patients has been an essential activity in the treatment intervention. The oldest types of diagnoses merely described what had been observed and then systematized the description. Since considerable confusion and inexactness have existed and since diagnoses are especially subject to local prejudice and the fashion of the times, recently diagnosis has been de-emphasized. This was a reaction against the misuse of diagnoses as mere labels and represented a trend throughout medicine toward looking at the patient as a person and abandoning the emphasis on diseases. It emphasized that individual patterns of psychopathology can be understood only in terms of the individual's life history. Yet such a person-oriented approach deprived the physician of the important prognostic and treatment implications of making a descriptive diagnosis.

A concise and helpful system of psychiatric descriptive diagnoses was developed by the American Psychiatric Association after World War II. Although there are a number of difficulties with this system and, indeed, many patients cannot be fitted clearly into any of its diagnostic categories, it does provide us with a useful method of communication, a basis for making therapeutic decisions, and a possibility of making prognostic statements. Although one schizophrenic patient is in many ways like another, obviously the individual who suffers from schizophrenia is unique in some features. In order to avoid the pitfalls of the diagnostic systems of the past, the descriptive diagnosis should be used only as a reminder that the patient has an illness characterized by a series of symptoms which, in fact, are his responses to stress and his attempts to deal restitutively with the problems at hand. Obviously, the patient does not have a diagnosis; we, the physicians, have the diagnosis. When the diagnosis and the patient do not fit, we must feel free to abandon diagnoses and return to the patient.

With this general approach descriptive diagnoses can work for us, rather than make us slaves to diagnostic systems. We can make a number of descriptive statements about each patient whom we observe, which, if expressed in commonly accepted language, are in fact a form of descriptive diagnosis. Thus, for example, for each patient we can and should make a social diagnosis that describes the present real-life social situation. Furthermore, we can make a character diagnosis in which we describe him as a person, describe his personality pattern, and say something about his characteristic life style, which includes his typical responses to stress. Such descriptive diagnoses are useful, since they convey some assessment of the premorbid situation of the patient as well as a description of the characteristic way in which he utilizes security operations in defending against stress. Next, medical diagnostic categories are included which describe any obvious physical disease. Finally, his psychiatric diagnosis can be made, which describes the major symptom complex in terms of accepted nomenclature. Thus, for example, we might have a diagnostic formulation as follows:

Social Diagnosis: A thirty-four-year-old Caucasian, married, male, and father of two children, who works regularly and successfully as a salesman and who apparently has an inadequate marital and social adjustment. *Personality Diagnosis:* The patient's life style is characterized by a passive approach to problems and a fairly passive way of handling aggression. He handles his feelings by isolating them, denying them, and repressing unacceptable thoughts. His character structure is that of a passive-aggressive person. *Medical Diagnosis:* Adequately healing superficial lacerations of both wrists. *Psychiatric Diagnosis:* Depressive reaction, moderate, characterized by feeling of despondency, hopelessness, and guilt, and manifested by self-destructive behavior (cutting his wrists).

Such a diagnostic approach conveys a fairly extensive description of an individual patient. It obviously communicates much more than a frequently applied label, "depression with attempted suicide." It tells us, for example, that this man has a job and works regularly, that he is unable to function in the family setting, and that in the past he has been able to handle his problems in his characteristic passive-aggressive manner. It tells us that because of some change, either in him or in his environment, his life style no longer suffices for the handling of stresses and that he has developed a depression that was superimposed upon his character structure. With such information, we can make a number of educated guesses as to treatment, prognosis, and etiology.

A second approach to illness is a dynamic description of the processes involved. In this situation, we can then move to a higher level of inference, where we no longer describe the behavior of the individual, but rather describe the mechanisms that are part of the motivational system resulting in the behavior. Our understanding of the dynamic mechanisms involved in certain kinds of symptom formation has been most helpful in the development of approaches to treatment, one of which is the subject of this book. For example, consider a person who has developed his response patterns in an emotional atmosphere lacking in or inconsistent in the availability of experiences that confirmed his views of himself as a worthwhile person and who had to grow to maturity in a family whose communications system was fraught with unpredictable corroborations and denials of the meaningfulness of his verbalizations. We are not surprised to find later an adult who gives evidence of low self-esteem and whose thinking is unclear. This kind of understanding of the dynamics of a symptom leads to important therapeutic interventions that have been found to be helpful. Nevertheless, dynamics are inferences and therefore not entirely trustworthy. Dynamic formulations can be used in designing a treatment intervention only so long as they are useful. If they turn out not to be useful, they must be discarded.

In terms of the theory of supportive care, the most useful approach to understanding the illness is a phenomenological one. This approach attempts to describe both the subjective and the objective aspects of the patient's illness. It not only describes behavior from the outside, as an observer would do, and relies on dynamic formulations which are speculative, but it also attempts to identify in minute detail the subjective experience of being ill. If, then, we look at the phenomenology of illness—and especially at the phenomenology of the kinds of illnesses that are appropriately treated by supportive care—we can understand the observed behavior in terms of three factors.

SYMPTOM AS RESTITUTION

The conceptual model of disease throughout medicine, including a conceptualization of psychological illnesses, has changed markedly during recent decades. Originally, in the modern era of medicine, the etiology of disease was conceived in terms of Koch's postulates. A bacterium or a noxious agent was identified in the diseased host. It was isolated in pure culture and reinjected into a new host; it could reproduce the same disease in the host, and then the organism or noxious agent was once again isolated. Such a conceptualization gave rise to the question, "What is the cause of this illness?" Very quickly we learned that even the simplest bacteriological diseases did not fit exactly into this model. We have learned that although, for example, the tubercle bacillus is a relevant etiological factor in clinical tuberculosis, it is not the "cause of tuberculosis." The cause of clinical tuberculosis is a very complex matter involving factors of genetics, resistance, hypersensitivity, virulence, the presence of a tubercle bacillus, and so forth. From this early conceptualization of the etiology of disease, through the influence of Hans Selye the conceptualization of disease moved to an etiological formulation in terms of diseases of adaptation. Symptoms were seen as adaptive phenomena or attempts at adaptation. This conceptualization was helpful in psychiatry. We could see and understand much of the behavior of patients in terms of the restitutive function of the symptoms. For example, a patient's low self-esteem could be understood in its relevance to his delusions of grandeur. We could begin to understand the delusions of a patient who thought that she was the Virgin Mary in terms of our recognition of the overwhelming amount of guilt she felt and her restitutional attempts from such guilt feelings. We could understand certain neurotic defense mechanisms in terms of a patient's way of dealing with stress. This approach, based on dynamic diagnoses, encouraged the recognition that meaning can be ascribed to almost all symptoms and that all behavior is meaningful.

Lately we have found reason once again to revise our conceptualization of illness as a process. The model of diseases as adaptive and restitutive symptoms no longer suffices in our understanding of the ill individual. Rather, we prefer to use the Stewart Wolf conceptualization of disease etiology, which sees the illness as the final common path of many factors. Within this kind of formulation we no longer ask, "What causes this illness?"; rather we ask, "What conditions, taken together, make it possible for these symptoms to emerge in this patient at this time?" This formulation recognizes that illness, symptom complexes, and the sick role itself are the final common paths of a number of forces impinging on the individual. It further recognizes that the picture of disease presented is a complex interaction of stress, adaptive capacity, and time. It emphasizes that the same stresses in a given individual at different times will not result in the same symptomatology and that the same stresses in different individuals will not produce the same symptomatology. In other words, it conceives of illness as a highly unique expression and communication of adaptive difficulty. It sees illness as a problem-stating and problem-solving mechanism.

Symptoms, then, can be seen as the final common path of all of the social, psychological, biological, genetic, economic, and other forces impinging on a patient at a particular time. They can be seen as attempts at restitution in dealing with emotional stresses.

THE IDENTITY PROBLEM

Who we are, and what we are, is constantly redetermined. Certainly it has been determined by our history, by what we have done, but it is also determined by our future, by what we are planning to do. Both past and future can be markedly altered by what is going on at present. A chronically ill person will retrospectively rewrite his history according to how he feels about himself and about his illness. He will similarly rewrite his anticipation of the future. Both of these reinterpretations influence how he is at the moment, and they influence how he thinks about himself as a person. If he has been ill for a considerable period of time, being ill becomes incorporated into his life style. Thus, he manifests his illness in all of his adaptations to all of the problems of living. The illness becomes markedly elaborated with secondary underpinnings of his character structure and thus becomes an essential part of his identity. For example, a patient who, neglected as a child, has been able to elicit the attention of significant figures in his life only by becoming the victim of minor or major calamities secondarily elaborates this behavior into a view of himself as a person against whom injustices are constantly perpetrated. It becomes clear from looking at illness in such a way that a treatment intervention that attempts to get the patient to give up certain symptoms must take this fact of secondary elaboration into account. It must recognize that someone who is chronically ill, physically or psychologically, has changed his identity to include in the self-concept the position of being an "ill person" and has constructed a security system that rests to a large extent on the altered expectations and demands of society on the ill person. The picture is further complicated by the fact that this identity is constantly reinforced by contact with others. It is a well-known psychological observation that identity develops and must be maintained through constant input into the self system from the outside world. When this input system is itself disturbed and reduced through the kinds of perceptual distortion and withdrawal seen in many chronically ill psychiatric patients, the distortions of identity can become extreme and the treatment intervention difficult. When the patient's disturbed, inappropriate, and otherwise unacceptable behavior causes the people in his environment to react with rejection, these reactions themselves, in cyclical fashion, become part of the patient's input system by a positive feedback that it is the task of the treatment intervention to interrupt.

Once the patient has been identified in the sick role by himself and by society, a number of important practices come to bear that tend firmly to cement the patient in the sick role. One of these is gratification dependency. In our society, which values competitive strivings and success, the adult is allowed little gratification of dependency. Once he has been defined as sick, however—once he has been officially determined to need medical attention—he can allow himself all kinds of gratification of dependency. He can stay in bed, he does not need to be productive, he can be waited on, and he can indulge in many other aspects of regression. This behavior is restitutive in allowing him, so to speak, to "recharge his battery"; at the same time, in a person who is chronically ill, such behavior has the danger of seducing the patient into a position of permanent regression. The difficult problem in the treatment of the chronically ill by supportive measures is to manage the dependency: to allow sufficient gratification for a maximal function and restoration from the sick role into the healthy role without at the same time permanently crippling the patient in the sick role. This problem will be discussed in much more detail in Chapter 4.

The second important aspect of the identity problem is

the issue of responsibility. With chronic psychiatric patients, for example, a person who acts in a certain way is identified as "sick." The same action—let us say, a person beating his wife—might be quite differently interpreted according to the role with which he is identified. If the wife calls the police, he is identified as a law-breaking criminal and will be taken to jail and subsequently tried by the courts. He is identified in the role of criminal, and his fate is quite different from that of a patient. If the wife is a religious person and the man is seen by a minister, he will be identified as a sinner, treatment will consist of interventions of a moral nature, and he can make restitution through the church. If the wife is psychiatrically sophisticated and brings the man to the attention of the medical profession, he is identified as sick. He is held to be "only partially responsible" for what he has done, and he is treated rather than punished or preached to. The patient and the physician, however, find themselves with a difficult problem of a dual structure. Since the behavior is the result of an illness and is thus a symptom, the patient is held not responsible. Just as we do not hold patients responsible for bleeding on the upholstery of a car after a traumatic injury, similarly we cannot hold the patient responsible for beating his wife in response to auditory hallucinations. And yet society does hold the person responsible for the kind of driving that led to the accident, and it does hold the person responsible for the kind of behavior involved in wife-beating. On the one hand we can say to the patient, "You are ill, and the manifestations of your illness are not within the possibility of your control; therefore, you are not responsible," but we must also say that this kind of action is not to be tolerated and must be controlled either by the patient or by those charged with his care. Within this difficult framework of conceiving of symptoms both as illness and as behavior which must be altered, the treatment situation becomes highly complicated, and the physician must be agile in his use of the conceptual framework to deal appropriately with the patient and the illness.

THE METAPHOR

How a patient expresses illness is determined not only by the personality of the patient, the restitutive forces in operation, and the conceptualization of the patient as occupying the sick role, but also to a large extent by the therapist who intervenes in the treatment situation. Most of the time—much more than we are aware, in fact—we as physicians dictate the metaphor in terms of which the patient approaches the sick role. A number of studies have been made which clearly indicate that the same patient with the same problems will focus on very different aspects of his illness depending on the doctor with whom he is talking. If he is being seen in the gastroenterological clinic he will have a tendency to focus on the gastrointestinal symptoms of his illness. The physician's known special interest, plus the selective listening and responding in which he engages, determines which area of the doctor-patient transaction is emphasized. For example, let us say that a patient comes to a physician with the opening statement "I have been feeling very bad lately. I worry all the time. I don't seem to be able to solve my problems. I have had to take a lot of antacids because I have much burning in my stomach." If this patient opens the therapeutic transaction with this kind of introduction, the gastroenterologist is prone to say, "Do you have this burning in the stomach when you have eaten or when your stomach is empty?" With this intervention the metaphor is determined, and, as he takes the history with attention to the gastrointestinal symptoms, the physician has the patient—at first identified only as being in the sick role— even further identified as having a gastrointestinal problem. They may spend many visits and many hours talking about the patient's gastrointestinal symptomatology. This example demonstrates the point that to a large extent the metaphor within which the patient expresses his illness is determined by the special interest of the physician.

Thus, when we see someone who is ill—indeed, chronically ill, as are those patients we think suitable for supportive care—we must know not only what he was like before he became ill, how he uses his symptoms restitutively, how society and the patient have identified him in the sick role and have used this identification as part of the life style of the person, but *also* something about his history of contacts with the treatment situation and how these have dictated the metaphor in which the patient "chooses" to relate his illness.

In summary, then, we might say that illness is the behavior of a person identified as a patient. Once he has been placed in the "sick role," what he does has been stated to be illness, and the one who intervenes is chosen to be the physician. Under this definition all of the forces previously identified in the doctor-patient relationship are used in order to help the patient to change in such a way that he is no longer ill and no longer identified in the sick role. This approach works well enough when the illness is temporary and the patient is willing to give up the sick role. The problems are great, however, when the patient is chronically ill and cannot give up his sick role. It is precisely this kind of patient that is in need of supportive treatment. Society demands improvement, the patient demands improvement, and the physician demands improvement; yet perhaps the major function of supportive care is to get the patient to function as best he can and to slow the decline of functioning. Within this framework, illness is seen as a state of impairment of function that can be altered by a treatment intervention focused on the assets of the patient rather than on his pathology. His basic defects perhaps cannot be altered, yet through the treatment intervention major changes in his ability to function can be made, which in themselves then become restitutive forces allowing for further improvement in functioning. The physician who treats the chronically ill who need supportive care must to some extent abandon his traditional position of being a pathologist focusing on what is wrong. He must turn about and focus on the assets and strengths the patient has remaining to him, taking the traditional position of the rehabilitation worker who takes stock of the assets of the patient and then rearranges them with the help of the patient in order to maximize function. Such an approach to the understanding of illness will allow for a treatment intervention which is helpful both to the patient and the physician in the problem of supportive care.

2

The Doctor-Patient Relationship

The relationship between a doctor and his patient may properly be regarded as a two-person transactional system. As is true of all complex, dynamic human relationships, each participant in this transaction has his own set of needs, fears, and expectancies. The degree to which the doctor successfully identifies these needs, fears, and expectancies in himself and in his patient will determine the degree to which the transaction can be successfully therapeutic. We are committed to the thesis that there is no such thing as a neutral relationship between a doctor and his patient. Each behavioral event in the transaction is significant in the outcome of the transaction, and every action on the part of the doctor will either contribute to or impede the therapeutic process.

In the therapeutic encounter between doctor and patient

the first requisite is that the doctor be less anxious than the patient. Although this requirement is usually easily met, the doctor's degree of comfort—as well as his effectiveness—in the situation will be increased if he is aware of his tendency to adopt what Balint has called the apostolic role of the doctor. By this phrase is meant the physician's need to have the patient respond to him in the role that he privately cherishes—be it as healer, magician, scientific investigator, experimenter, friendly advisor, advocate, and special pleader, or any of a broad variety of other such unspoken images. Although the treatment of any condition will be impaired if the patient must respond to such private needs on the part of the therapist, in the supportive care of the chronic conditions of which we write in this book such a requirement imposes a demand on these patients which they are usually quite unable to fulfill. Not only must the doctor be aware of any tendency on his part to bring a hidden agenda to the meeting between doctor and patient, he must also make himself aware of those unspoken needs which the patient brings to the transaction. Does he have a wish to be a helpless infant, loyal son, inexpert apprentice in the art of living, love object, or to play some other role which his chronic illness has made him prone to adopt?

Patients for whom supportive care is the treatment of choice have had difficulties in so many areas of their functioning that the complaint that they present to the doctor is frequently determined by the manifest interests of that doctor. The same patient would emphasize palpitations, diarrhea, headache, or anxiety depending on whether the sign outside the doctor's office said cardiology, gastroenterology, neurology, or psychiatry. The doctor-patient encounter, then, must be regarded as a medium of human interchange in which the doctor is not constrained to accept only the denotative communication which the patient makes; he must also attempt to make himself aware of the connotative, latent, or metaphorical communications that are always an important part of the transaction. The actual spoken words of the transaction in rendering supportive care can be equally well carried out in the metaphor of cardiology, proctology, psychiatry, or any other specialty as long as the basic principles are adhered to. We must learn to listen to the music, not the words, and we must understand the themes of the communication. The therapist chooses the metaphor of his response on the basis of the patient's ability to handle undisguised communication. Generally, the more frightened the patient, and the lower his self-esteem, the more distance he requires for communication. As a rule of thumb, the patient himself is best able to judge when he is ready to communicate directly. Thus the doctor should make it possible for the patient to communicate directly in words. He does so by demonstrating his interest with a nonjudgmental, noncritical, and nondemanding attitude; but it should be the chronic patient who initiates taking the communication out of the metaphor.

Not only must the doctor attempt to make himself aware of the expectancies he brings to the transaction, he must also focus on those standards of human behavior by which he assesses the degree of pathology in the patient. That is to say, how does he judge what in the patient's behavior should be regarded as "normal" or "healthy" and what as "abnormal" or "sick"?

Perhaps the criterion most ready to hand is the behavior of the doctor himself. In applying this criterion, however, the doctor must be alert both to its potential for providing subtleties of insightful awareness and to the degree to which it can completely vitiate useful objective assessment. Is the patient intelligent? Here the doctor must keep in mind that he must compare the patient with the subjective norms that he has acquired in his dealings with all of his fellow men. Compared with the doctor himself and with his medical colleagues (who, as a group, measure from one to two standard deviations above the mean of intelligence), it would be easy to say of a patient of average intelligence that he is woefully dull.

On the other hand, when he realizes that in some subtle way the patient's thought processes, as revealed in his rationale for behaving in a particular way, have led him to conclusions that to the doctor seem illogical or that can be made logical only when the doctor supplies significant links in the logical chain, links which have been omitted in the patient's account, the doctor may have hit upon the first evidence of serious thought pathology that has previously gone unrecognized and that underlies many of the patient's difficulties in living. It will thus be seen that using the doctor as the criterion against which to assess the patient will affect the doctor-patient relationship and can aid or impede coming to conclusions that will be useful in the management of the patient's illness.

Another criterion for the assessment of health versus illness has been the measure of happiness that the patient's behavior brings to him. Although it is generally true that the patient is unlikely to bring himself into the doctor-patient relationship if he is happy with his behavior and its consequences, the equation of happiness with health seems to us to fail as an adequate criterion. One thinks of many persons whose motivation for significant contributions to healthy change has been their dissatisfaction with things as they are.

A purely statistical criterion has often been utilized in assessing health or illness. This very useful approach, which has much scientific relevance to such an assessment, is, however, difficult to apply to such complex human behavioral phenomena as social interaction or the interplay of thought and judgment. Our statistical norms or ranges of normal values of measures of these parameters are not comparable to such traditional measures of healthy functioning as PBI, sedimentation rate, or hemoglobin. Moreover, a purely statistical criterion carries with it the temptation to utilize it as a moral value and to assess statistically significant deviations from it as "bad" as well as "sick." One has only to review the history of the changed view of a social phenomenon such as slavery to recognize that such norms are impermanent and therefore of limited value.

In our view any criterion for health must view the person's success in the important areas of social relationships, work, and leisure and must find that in functioning in these areas the person is capable of an empathic awareness of the effect of his behavior on the people around him. To this criterion we should add a longitudinal aspect: a healthy person should have a history of growth in these areas to a point where satisfactory functioning has been achieved and maintained over the course of the life one is reviewing. Sometimes the surest indication of a disease process is to be found in evidence of a gradual erosion of adequate functioning in one of these important aspects of living. Indeed, those chronically ill patients who can respond to supportive care are precisely those in whom one sees just such a decline in function historically and who have remained or who become so inward-directed that they become insensitive to their fellow men.

In the diagnosis of chronic schizophrenia much has been made of this evidence of decline of function. The Kraepelinian view of dementia praecox took cognizance of this longitudinal deterioration, and in the earlier history of psychiatry the assumption was made that the course of the illness was one of gradual deterioration from healthy functioning in young adulthood to complete and irreversible dementia in later years. It was the significant contribution of Eugen Bleuler to the study of psychopathology that the course of this illness did not inevitably terminate in dementia, and this view he reflected in his substitution of the term "schizophrenia" for "dementia praecox." We now know that the decline of mental functioning to a state of dementia was related to the limiting and stultifying environments to which we subjected these patients in "caring" for them by participating in their almost total alienation from their families and communities when we collected them in asylums and became the custodians of every aspect of their lives.

We have learned that a person's behavior is not simply the result of his pathology or his character structure. Rather, behavior is the observable data, the final common path of a complex interaction between character structure, pathology, and role expectancy. The patient responds to the doctor in part in terms of the expectancy of the transaction. When physicians were hopeless about schizophrenics, when they believed with Kraepelin in the relentless, progressive deterioration of the minds of these patients, when they reinforced this pathology by "putting them away" in asylums, then patients responded by "deteriorating." When the role expectancy has been changed, however, to conform to modern concepts of brief hospitalization at times of crisis combined with supportive care which maximizes the patient's ability to function, mental deterioration is not seen.

Supportive care includes working with a patient's abilities and strengths while minimizing the impact of his disabilities. In caring for a chronic patient we are aware of the decline of function that his history reveals, and we do not delude ourselves (nor do we demand of the patient) that he will necessarily return to his best level of functioning or surpass it. But we do support those qualities of his personality which are relatively undamaged by his illness. We support his right to have a relationship which recognizes his human worth, and we support him in maintaining his significant contacts. Hospitalization is still sometimes necessary, as will be discussed in Chapter 8, but it should serve as a prelude to—rather than as a substitute for—real contact with a real community.

In supportive care the doctor-patient relationship should be characterized by its being accepting, nonjudgmental, and relatively demand-free. In accepting the patient, the doctor takes an attitude which reflects the fact that he values the human worth of the patient and has not allowed the alienation which chronic illness frequently imposes on the patient's relationships to adulterate this new relationship. In supportive care the doctor is nonjudgmental in that he does not pass moral judgment on the worth-whileness of the patient or on his behavior; rather, he exercises his judgment as to the appropriateness or inappropriateness, the health or illness of the patient's behavior. In supportive care the relationship is demand-free in that it does not make a continuation of the relationship conditional on the patient's meeting certain stated or implied demands from the doctor. The future of the relationship is both implicit and explicit and does not depend on the patient's achieving any particular goal stated by the doctor.

We referred earlier to unspoken needs that the patient brings to the doctor-patient transaction. Whatever the specific role that the patient seems to adopt in the relationship, it is clear that a significant degree of dependency pervades his needs (see Chapter 4) and, as a corollary of this dependency, that he imbues the doctor with qualities of magic and omnipotence that, although not realistic, can be used by the doctor as an extremely potent tool in helping the patient. Assuming, of course, that the doctor is not seduced by the patient's needs into believing in his own omnipotence (see Chapter 5), he can lend his strength to the patient's weakened ego. At first, if the patient is overwhelmed and unable to deal with reality, the doctor will take over nearly all decisions for the patient. He will help the patient to order and manage his life in its minutest details. By selective attention in how he listens to the patient's description of his irrational fears, he will demonstrate that he is not overwhelmed by these feared situations and that the patient can borrow his strength, thus establishing in the patient a growing feeling that, by emulating the doctor's concern over goal-directed activity, the patient too can hope to rid himself of the fears that now beset him. Just as he imputes to the doctor greater than life-sized powers and strength, so does the patient endow all that pertains to the doctor with some of the same magic. Taking pills prescribed by the doctor symbolizes to the patient partaking of some of that strength with which to manage his adversity. Even the doctor's office can prove a reassuring place for a sick patient; it is not unusual for a patient to come and sit in the waiting room at times when he has no appointment or even to drive past the doctor's office to reassure himself that this source of strength is still available to him. He may call the doctor's office, ostensibly to check on the time of his next appointment, although he has an appointment slip, and this action too serves as a reminder that this important relationship—which we know is made more significant because it is not threatened by his illness, as are many of his other relationships—is real and can be counted on to continue.

Just as the patient has learned to fear that supportive relationships may be threatened by his inability to meet the needs and expectancy of the other (father, teacher, doctor), so the relationship may be threatened by the opposite turn of events—a marked improvement. In the usual doctor-patient relationship the patient presents himself with symptoms that are "removed" by the physician, and the result is the termination of that relationship. The reader can easily see the difficulties involved in such an expectancy of termination on the part of either the patient or the physician when the improvement is entirely due to and dependent on the continued supportive relationship. Although the frequency and type of contact can be altered as the patient's functioning improves, the relationship must be continued indefinitely to support the therapeutic gains that have been achieved.

As the patient learns to be confident of the predictability and reliability of this relationship, some of his anxieties regarding the relationship itself become manageable, and he can devote more of his energies to the task of learning from his mentor-therapist the techniques of attending more to what he does and less to what he thinks and feels. As the patient grows in his skills of attending to what he does and to its consequences, it will be seen that he is exercising more adequate adaptive functions and that he has less need to borrow the therapist's ego in such a total fashion as he once did. This transition represents one of the most critical periods in the doctor-patient relationship. Because of the doctor's natural reluctance to continue in this charismatic role and because of the patient's understandable urge to function autonomously, it is easy for doctor and patient to conspire in arranging plans for the patient that the patient is unable to complete. It is precisely because of the weakened nature of the schizophrenic patient's ego that he is much more vulnerable to failures than is the normal person. Even minor failures devastate him and remove important gains that he has made in the supportive relationship. It is easy for him to misinterpret the doctor's encouragement to achieve and to view it as a condition on which the future of the relationship depends. It is vital to the patient's continued good functioning that the doctor not imply an end to the relationship and that his activities not be interpreted by the patient as a demand on him. Each suggestion, then, on the part of the patient that he undertake a new and higher level of adjustment must be interpreted by the therapist as a question from the patient that has the latent meaning, "Is it necessary for me to function better to warrant my continuing to see you?" The doctor, therefore, must be sure that his communications, both overt and covert, carry the meaning, "I accept you as a person worthy of my concern no matter what your level of achievement." Another potential pitfall in the doctor-patient relationship occurs when the therapist is inclined to react to increasingly healthy behavior on the part of the patient by implying a diminution or even a termination of the therapy. The patient is likely to interpret this implication as a reinforcement of his sick behavior and a negative reinforcement of healthy behavior. He is, therefore, likely to respond to such a suggestion of termination by becoming sicker again in order to regain the concern and care of the physician.

Although we have been discussing the doctor-patient relationship as a model for the helping situation, the helper can obviously be some other representative of the helping situation, such as a social worker, nurse, psychologist, or minister. One can conceptualize the helping relationship in supportive care as being a teaching and learning situation in which, through selective inattention to pathological thought and feeling and selective attention to actions and their consequences, the patient is assisted in assuming a role of hopeful expectancy. This role is defined through the communication as imposing certain limitations on what the patient can expect from himself, while minimizing guilt and lowered self-esteem in regard to these limitations. He learns to behave "as if" he were not suffering from these limitations, and he learns that the experience of illness has heuristic value for him. That is to say, the symptoms of his illness are remembered and serve as warning signs for him should they recur in his behavior. He is helped by the physician to avoid situations in which he is likely to fail. He finds reassurance in the doctor-patient relationship; the doctor listens to him, reflects back his concerns about himself, and implies a future to the relationship. The major emphasis must be on the here and now, precisely for the reason that any conversation about fantasied future events removes the patient from the vitally necessary task of paying attention to his present behavior and its consequences. Yet the future must at all times be maintained open by the ongoing relationship with the therapist. It is this open future that carries the patient through many painful crises until he can reorganize at a more adaptive level where his own successful coping experiences can keep the future open. Then the therapeutic relationship can be altered to allow for more independence on the part of the patient. On the other hand, termination will usually result in severe exacerbation of symptoms unless the patient has defined the helping situation so broadly that he can see other representatives as readily available future therapists.

3

Theory of Treatment

The treatment transaction is carried on within the framework of one of the oldest and most highly systemized human interactions. The participants in this transaction, one identified as a patient, the other as a therapist, engage with each other for the purpose of relieving or changing some form of feeling or behavior in the patient. The changes occurring in the therapist are not the primary concern of the treatment transaction, although they must indeed be understood and recognized for the proper management of treatment. Both parties come to the treatment situation with a history of many relationships which bear considerable similarity to it. A child-parent relationship is the prototype of all human relationships and closely parallels the patient-physician transaction since it includes the dimensions of dependence and independence, helplessness and improvement, growth and regression, development and arrest, being in the care of others and caring for others. Of course, there are other relationships later than the child-parent one in our human society that also prepare the patient for the therapeutic transaction. These interactions include those between the devout and the priest, the apprentice and the magician, the medical patient and the physician, and the student and the teacher. All of these relationships have in common that the one goes to the other for the purpose of getting help, explanation, care, and concern. Every person who enters the state of patienthood is prepared, in part, for such a transaction by his lived history of other relationships that involve a situation in which he is dependent and moves toward being able to help himself, in which he does not understand and moves toward understanding, in which he cannot control and moves toward obtaining the tools of control. Similarly, the therapist comes to the treatment transaction with a history of having been a patient, a child, and a student, and of having mastered these states. As a therapist, now, he takes the adult-caring role, handling his own needs for care by caring for others. Erikson describes the final state of maturity as ego-integrity, which is characterized by a capacity to adapt oneself to the triumphs and disappointments of existence and a capacity to care for others in the human encounter.

The psychotherapeutic relationship is the most intimate human relationship possible. The formalities and the rules of the patient-therapist transaction allow for extremely rapid movement toward the intimacies necessary for treatment. It is a constant wonder to us how thoroughly the tradition of intimacy is incorporated into the patient-physician relationship. One need only remind himself that a physician, after only a few minutes of introduction, is given license by the patient and by society to explore every orifice, to probe the intimate secret recesses of the unconscious, or physically to lay open the patient's abdomen in order to alter anatomy by surgical intervention. In this medical transaction, the patient brings so much trust to the physician that he will literally place his life in his hands, without knowing any more about him than the fact that he wears the medical badge. Each one of us, as a therapist, inherits all of the feelings and attitudes which society holds toward the medical magician. Outside of this tradition, human relationships take a very different course. Most relationships move much more slowly, and it may take years to build up enough trust and confidence for one participant to trust the other with his life or to allow the type of physical and psychological intimacies that are inherent in the medical transaction. Indeed, certain of our social taboos are never transgressed in relationships other than the patient-doctor transaction.

The medical transaction that is the model for the psychotherapeutic engagement is conducted in terms of an unspoken contract in which the therapist takes responsibility for treating the patient and in which the patient agrees to be treated and to compensate the therapist for his services. Built into this contract is the patient's hope, or at least suspicion, that he can live life differently, that better functioning is possible for him, and that he can exist with less anguish and pain. For the therapist, accepting a patient for treatment implies that he can intervene in some way helpful to the patient. Thus, built into the contract is the concept of the open future. The open future implies to the patient that the therapist anticipates change in the direction of the therapeutic goals. It implies that the doctor can intervene in some way to offer care, to be helpful, and to keep the future open.

The patient comes for help and relief, but for what purposes does the therapist come to the transaction? Much has been written in the literature on therapy about the need for a patient to pay in order for the therapeutic process to be successful. We should agree as to the need for payment, although frequently payment is not in the form of money. In order for treatment to be efficient and to minimize the antitherapeutic confusion of roles, it is essential that the therapist define for himself how he will obtain his gratification from the treatment transaction without interfering with the primary therapeutic goal of the process. The difference between the social relationship and the therapeutic relationship lies in the equality and immediacy of gratification for each participant. In the therapeutic relationship, the therapist is in charge and manages the transaction for the patient's benefit, that is to say, to fulfill the therapeutic intent. His gratification comes from financial rewards, research rewards, teaching rewards, or other gratifications related to his professional role, or from combinations of these. On the other hand, in the social relationship no one of the participants is in charge, and each has the right to expect equal and reciprocal gratification. The social relationship is not managed to benefit one participant or the other, but rather is an attempt to extract an equal amount of benefit for both. When the differences between the social and the therapeutic relationship are blurred, the transaction becomes unnecessarily complicated and at times impossible. Similarly, when the rewards for the therapist in the treatment transaction are not clearly defined to him, there is some risk that he may attempt to obtain his rewards in such a way that the patient's therapy is interfered with. Generally, money is the simplest way in which a patient can pay a therapist. Of course, satisfaction of research interests and teaching interests are also rewards built into the role of the therapist. It is impossible for a therapist to treat a patient effectively when the rewards for therapy are not clearly defined. Then, too, there is the danger of the therapist's exploitation of the therapeutic transaction for personal and neurotic rewards that seriously interfere with the therapeutic intent.

As we noted in Chapter 2, because of the highly charged nature of the therapeutic transaction and because of the historical roots of the patient-doctor relationship in the child-parent relationship, it is impossible to conceive of the medical transaction as ever being neutral. It must necessarily be either therapeutic or antitherapeutic; that is to say, it must help the patient to move in the direction of improved adaptive capacity and functioning or it will hinder his movement in that direction. No relationship, be it ever so brief, involving a transaction between a patient and a therapist can be conceived of as neutral. There are many reminders of this highly charged nature of the therapeutic relationship. It immediately becomes apparent that ordinary social interactions assume a different character in the therapeutic engagement. When we walk down a hall and greet a colleague with, "How are you?" we expect him to reply in terms of the usual social conspiracy with, "Fine," while grinning in a friendly manner no matter how he really feels. If he stops to tell us how he is, and if he takes twenty minutes of our time to complain about his family, his work, his tax bills, and his sexual life, we would probably get angry and judge him presumptuous in not playing the game; or we would assume that he has become seriously disturbed and therefore can no longer participate in the expected social transaction. On the other hand, when a patient comes into our office and we close the door, then we are identified as the doctor; and when we say, "How are you?" both he and we know that now he must really tell us how it goes with him and that now we really are prepared to try to understand and help him. In each of the transactions described—the social and the medical—the same words are spoken, but the intent and the effect are entirely different. In the social transaction there is an understanding that we really do not want to know how it is with the other person when we ask him how things are going. Such exchanges may be translated as, "I recognize you. Please do the same for me." In the medical transaction such a question is expected to bring a complete and truthful reply and implies that we are interested and willing to listen.

Thus, hope and trust on the patient's part and care and concern on the therapist's part must invariably be components of the treatment transaction. But obviously these attitudes are only the skeleton which underlies treatment, and upon this skeleton is built technique. In general, the techniques of psychotherapy may be divided into two major categories: expressive (insight, definitive, analytic) and repressive (supportive, palliative, activity). Expressive techniques of psychotherapy are most useful with patients who are described as belonging to the neurotic and character disorder diagnostic categories. These techniques consist of allowing the patient to discover things about himself which are out of awareness, so that he can use these discoveries in an expansion of knowledge about himself to obtain increased opportunities for the mastery of his own destiny. Expressive techniques are contraindicated for the psychotic patient or for the patient classified as borderline psychotic. When such techniques are applied, they tend to accelerate the disorganization of the patient. With such psychotic patients, repressive techniques are most applicable. These techniques consist of helping the patient to differentiate clearly between what is real and what is fantasy, what is inside and what is outside, between wish, dream, delusion on the one hand, and action on the other. But even with repressive techniques, an attempt is made at times to explore the history of present attitudes and feelings in order to promote a sense of mastery.

All psychotherapy can be described in five essential steps. Depending on whether one is using expressive or supportive techniques, any one of these steps may be emphasized whereas others are de-emphasized. Step 1 of any psychotherapeutic transaction must necessarily be the development of trust that follows upon the therapist's willingness to engage in order to understand. Step 2 is confrontation. After forming the relationship, we help the patient to see how we view his feelings, thoughts, and behavior. In essence we hold up a mirror to the patient and say, "Look, it seems to me that this is what you feel; this is what you are doing; this is what you are saying. Are you aware of that?" In supportive care we tend to emphasize this step by asking the patient to become increasingly aware of his behavior and the consequences of his behavior. Step 3 in all psychotherapy involves a detailed exploration of the history of present attitudes, feelings, and behavior. It is this phase that is much emphasized in expressive psychotherapies, especially in psychoanalytic techniques. It is this step that is minimized in the supportive care of patients. Step 4 in psychotherapeutic transactions consists of the exploration of alternative ways of handling present problems. In supportive techniques, this aspect is emphasized, whereas in expressive methods it is generally carried out in the process of working through. In supportive care the therapist takes a very active part in step 4, even to the extent of training the patient in acceptable methods of handling problems, of exploring with him the consequences of these methods, and of suggesting alternative ways of behaving. In this aspect of treatment, the patient and the therapist explore alternative ways of interpreting the world, other ways of looking at feelings, and other ways of handling interpersonal relationships. Step 5 of the psychotherapeutic endeavor consists of helping the patient to try out these different ways of behaving and feeling. In expressive techniques this is primarily left to the attention of the patient, but in supportive care, step 5 is very much a part of the treatment transaction. Unless the patient is helped to try out some new methods of approaching life, he obviously cannot improve. No patient has ever gotten well in the consulting room. Patients only get well in life. With a chronically ill patient it takes a great deal of skilled management of the treatment transaction to give him sufficient security to attempt some new ways of managing the world. If these new approaches to life are successful and are reinforced by reality and by the therapist, they can eventually become part of the patient's life style and lead to permanent changes of behavior, attitudes, and feelings. For the patient, the changes in behavior occur in an orderly fashion. He moves from an unawareness of himself and of his reality to an ability to observe and report his behavior. He can say, "This is the way I behave; this is how I interpret my reality." As he improves and develops increasing ability to be reflective about himself, he can say, "Oops, there I did it again," displaying a new capacity to stand back and look at himself. As treatment progresses, he can begin to change his behavior, and he might be able to say, "There, I almost did it again." Eventually, as the change in his behavior is reinforced and rewarded sufficiently to become part of his new life style, the patient will remember, "This is what I used to do—that kind of thing—but now I don't have to do it any more." Eventually the change in his behavior is so thoroughly incorporated into his life style that the patient can say, "I'm the kind of person who no longer does the kind of thing I used to do."

From this discussion of the changes occurring in the course of psychotherapy it is apparent that improvement is generally in the direction of the patient's accepting and assuming increased responsibility for his own behavior and destiny. It may at first appear paradoxical that to relieve the patient of responsibility for his thoughts and feelings, for his fantasies and wishes, should also lead to increased responsibility for his actions. Yet that is exactly what happens. As the patient learns to differentiate clearly his internal turmoil and agony from his behavior, he can also learn not to hold himself responsible for the former, whereas he is responsible for the latter. In supportive care we show the patient over and over again that what counts is what he does, that he is responsible for his behavior, and that he must accept control over his own destiny. That is not to be confused with demanding from him a level of functioning that he cannot possibly reach.

All therapeutic transactions involve the development of dependency. In Chapter 4 we shall describe some of the technical problems of managing dependency in order to maximize the therapeutic effort. Not only dependency but in the larger sense the entire relationship between the therapist and the patient must constantly be monitored by the therapist so as to move in the direction of as much therapeutic gain as possible. The major vehicle of the therapeutic movement is obviously the relationship of the patient to the therapist. This relationship is a potent therapeutic tool, fundamental to which is the development of trust. It is this aspect of the treatment transaction that makes it so difficult to treat the chronic schizophrenic patient. We know that the first relationships between the infant and the mother are dependent on the ability of the infant to develop a trusting attitude toward her and toward external reality. Once such trust has been developed, future relationships are possible, but it is precisely in this area of trust that one can see the major incapacity of the schizophrenic patient. Such a person has great difficulty developing a working and consistent trust in anyone or anything. Most of our techniques of supportive care as described in this book are attempts to help a person who has been unable to develop such a trusting relationship with others to redevelop an investment in the world. To foster the development of trust requires constant appraisal and awareness of both the patient's participation in the transaction and the effect of the therapist on the patient. The unfolding of the trusting investment of the patient in the therapist and in reality is like a delicate flower that must be nurtured, stimulated, supported, and guided and that, with the slightest mismanagement, wilts. The development of the trusting relationship is indeed a crucial issue in the successful treatment of the schizophrenic, and yet it is precisely this area in which he has the greatest difficulty. Thus, as therapists, we find ourselves in the difficult situation of knowing that in order to improve permanently the patient must develop trust in the therapeutic transaction, in external reality, and in himself; at the same time it is precisely his inability to invest this trust in anything or anyone that is his basic defect. Working and consistent trust can develop only in the safety of the therapeutic transaction. With appropriate support and proper management, this trust can then be generalized to other situations.

In this chapter we have attempted to describe the process of the psychotherapeutic transaction in supportive care, but we have paid little attention to the content of the transaction. In Part II of this book, which is devoted to practice, we deal more specifically with the management of the particular content. In general, however, it can be said that dealing with content of the transaction must be directed and organized in a fivefold manner. First, as the patient talks about his feelings, his thoughts, his activities, and his fantasies in the atmosphere of acceptance in the therapeutic transaction, he can experience some lessening of anxiety and some feeling of mastery over the content of his distress. Second, a discussion of the content of the therapeutic transaction is used by the therapist to help the patient in improving his reality-testing. As the patient describes his reality and compares it with the reality of the therapist, he can begin to deal with the suspicion, at least, that other interpretations of reality than his own are possible. Third, the content of the therapeutic hour can be dealt with to demonstrate acceptance of the patient by the therapist regardless of thoughts or feelings. It can be used to demonstrate a nonjudgmental attitude by the therapist, that is to say, a nonjudgmental attitude in terms of deciding whether the patient is morally good or bad. Certainly, the therapist makes medical judgments and judgments about the patient's functioning and behavior in order to help the patient to try out new modes of behavior in the safety of the therapeutic engagement. So to speak, in the atmosphere of acceptance and trust, the patient can send up trial balloons to see how the therapist feels about anticipated behavior. Thus, fourth, the patient can use the therapeutic transaction as a private laboratory in which to experiment with attitudes and behavior prior to launching them in life. Fifth, the content can be used to teach the patient the attitudes of others toward him. It is in the safety of the therapeutic transaction that he can learn to cope with certain minimal rejections and failures. It is here, in the safety of his trusting relationship to the therapist, that he can steel himself for the real world. The therapist can help him to learn patterns of behavior in order to develop the "as if" role; as the patient successfully masters the task of increasing his effectiveness in living and taking on the "as if normal" role, new technical problems arise for the therapist. Unless the therapist remembers constantly how sick the patient is, unless he can remind himself of the shallowness of the patient's adaptive capacities, he may fall into the trap of joining the world in believing that the patient is not ill. Certainly, the successfully treated patient who is receiving supportive care can appear to the world as healthy. It takes the skilled therapist only a few moments of probing, however, to reconfirm the extent of the patient's disorganization underlying the façade of adaptation maintained by supportive care. This façade, which may assume permanence in the life of the patient, can be likened to the snowcap on a dormant volcano; the subterranean fires are not extinguished and may erupt at any moment as the balance of internal and external forces is altered.

4

Management
of
Dependency

———————————————◆
———————————————◆
———————————————◆

In every therapeutic relationship the patient develops dependence on the therapist even before the beginning of the formal therapy sessions. By the very fact that the patient places himself in the role of being a patient and chooses a therapist, he accepts dependency. This dependency can be defined as a state of being that is influenced and determined by or conditional upon the therapist. As we mentioned in Chapter 3, the prototype for the therapeutic relationship is the parent-child relationship, also a situation of managed dependency. The child, like the patient, moves from a position of great and real dependence to increasing independence and finally to a position of having dependency gratified primarily through symbolic representation of the dependency-gratifying figure. Much has been written about the problems of dependency. There are many warnings about the dangers of prolonged overdependence of the patient on the therapist. In specific psychotherapeutic systems various names are attached to the dependency that the patient develops: transference, parataxic distortion, predominance of the past, and others. It is generally agreed that the development of dependency is a necessary part of any psychotherapeutic transaction. It is inconceivable that therapy can go on without the development of such dependency. It is also generally agreed that, as the patient grows and develops in the psychotherapeutic transaction, he must move to a position of giving up some of his dependency. There is much disagreement as to what extent this relinquishing actually occurs. Although we speak of the resolution of the transference, experienced therapists know that a portion of the positive transference remains as a lifelong attachment to the symbol of the good mother—the therapist; indeed, it continues to work as a psychotherapeutic force.

In the treatment of the chronic schizophrenic patient, the problem of dependency becomes especially complicated. As we have previously mentioned, the development of a consistent trust in anything or anyone is an extremely difficult task for the schizophrenic patient. Yet he must act as though he trusts something or someone. He must be willing to accept on faith, like all human beings, that tomorrow will come, and, although he realizes that perhaps it will not, he must plan and act as though it would. Similarly, he must develop some trust in another human being. To live in a world in which he can invest no trust in anyone is impossible. Each man is perforce a member of a society of men, and social relationships are built on individual human relationships, the core of which is the feeling of trust. In situations that produce a major rupture of trust in one's fellow human beings, such as concentration camps, persons may be so betrayed by their fellow men that they are irreparably changed thereafter. Similarly, schizophrenic patients frequently are unable to develop trust in anyone because they, too, feel totally betrayed by their fellow men. Whether this lack is the result of betrayal by the mother or is due to a defect in the patient's ability to develop trust is not important for the therapeutic task. The fact that the patient has great difficulty developing a trusting relationship —a dependence—is a major problem of therapy. Obviously, the patient is caught in a most difficult position. One of his difficulties is that he cannot develop trust in anyone. Yet in order to be helped, in order to change his behavior and his feelings, he must develop trust in the therapist, or at least be willing to take a chance on developing trust. Thus, he must take the risk of developing a dependence on a fellow human being. This task assumes major importance in the therapeutic effort with the chronic schizophrenic patient. We have outlined in Chapters 3 and 10 a number of techniques for helping a patient to develop trust enough to form a dependency. These techniques include the offering of a consistent and totally reliable relationship that does not demand a closeness beyond the patient's tolerance. At the beginning of the development of the dependency, the chronic schizophrenic patient cannot tolerate even the slightest unreliability. Appointments must be kept on time—must not be cancelled. The therapist must be available and must withstand constant testing of his availability, consistency, and reliability. The therapist must manage the distance between himself and the patient and must maintain it throughout all the tests that the patient will put him to, including hostility, seduction, exacerbation of symptoms, and remission. The therapist may need to withstand such maneuvers for years without feeling secure that the patient finally trusts him and has developed a useful therapeutic dependency. Even when the therapeutic relationship is going well, a therapist may suddenly be surprised to face a new test of his reliability and dependability. In many therapeutic relationships the history of the therapist's reliability and dependability does little to reassure the patient. He may have been well managed for years, the therapist may have made no errors and have demonstrated no unreliability, and then, on one occasion, he is not available to the patient; the patient may then react with the feeling that he has once again confirmed what he knew all along, that no fellow human being can be relied upon.

It is obviously necessary for the patient to have enough trust in the therapist and to develop enough dependency to be willing to change his behavior on the basis of the therapist's direction. Much of what the patient does in the therapeutic transaction is motivated by his wish to maintain the relationship with the therapist, since he feels so constantly threatened with abandonment. Since he has so little self-esteem he is evaluating the wishes of the therapist, both spoken and unspoken, and constantly attempting to please. Such dependency is useful in the therapeutic transaction if the therapist can monitor it precisely and can manage to convey clear signals to the patient in terms of the kind of behavior and approach to reality that are acceptable and that will help the patient.

If dependency is well managed, if a patient is able to develop some consistent trust in and therefore dependence on the therapist, and if he can use this trust and this dependency in altering his behavior outside of the therapeutic transaction, eventually the patient can widen his trust and allow himself to develop a dependence (albeit tenuous) on others. In a well-managed therapy, the following process unfolds: The patient develops a dependence on the therapist; he relies on and trusts in the reality of the psychotherapeutic transaction after many tests of it; finally he makes an attempt to depend on reality outside of the psychotherapeutic transaction and to invest other human beings with trust by allowing himself to become dependent on them. Of course, he is always on guard; always ready to withdraw into the shell; always ready to say, "Everyone has turned out to be as unreliable and undependable as I knew they would be in the first place," while at the same time creating situations that demonstrate this effect. Such a patient behaves much like a testing, exploring snail. He sticks his head out very tentatively, and if he touches the slightest bit of rejection or unreliability, he withdraws into the shell. Each time it happens he stays in the shell a little longer and eventually refuses to come out for long periods of time. The patient is going to find many rejections in real life outside of the therapeutic transaction, and he is going to find that others are not entirely dependable. Throughout this difficult stage the therapist must help the patient. He must help him to extend his trust to others. He must help him to live as if he could depend on tomorrow to come; as if he could depend on others to do what needs to be done; as if he could depend on some predictions of other people's behavior. The therapist can help by preparing the patient for what may happen. For example, before attempting a relationship outside of psychotherapy, the patient might discuss all possible outcomes of this relationship with the therapist and, so to speak, work them through by considering all alternatives. Having thus prepared himself, he will be less surprised by anything that happens and, in effect, will develop a trust in his own ability to cope. He can gain some feeling of being able to depend on his predictions and indeed, if this stage goes well, the next stage is the development of trust in self. He can then be viewed as having moved from patienthood to selfhood. Thus, having developed some trust and dependency with the therapist, having proved that it is safe to do so, having enlarged his trust and dependency to take in others in the outside world, and having dealt with his experiments in depending on others in the therapeutic transaction by learning to predict the possible outcome of such dependency, the patient, it may be hoped, can finally move to a state of trusting himself and relying on himself. For the healthy person, of course, this stage is one of confidence and satisfaction. The human being who can trust himself and depend on himself is never alone and will never be let down. Most neurotic patients who are liberated by the discovery of self-reliance recognize that problems of loneliness and insecurity are solved permanently only in this way. The chronic schizophrenic patient cannot develop this stage to the fullest. He can never really trust himself entirely and he can never really relieve his loneliness and isolation from within; but he can move surprisingly far in this direction. In fact, he can even move to the final step of human development and maturation that allows others to depend on him. He can care for others and have others depend on him. As a parent, as a teacher, as a creative person, he develops a stage of ego integrity that Erik Erikson describes thus:

> Only in him who in some way has taken care of things and people and has adapted himself to the triumphs and disappointments inherent to being, the originator of others or the generator of products and ideas—only in him may gradually ripen the fruit of these . . . stages [of maturity]. I know no better word for it than ego integrity. Lacking a clear definition, I shall point to a few constituents of this state of mind. It is the ego's accrued assurance of its proclivity for order and meaning. It is a post-narcissistic love of the human ego—not of the self—as an experience which conveys some world order and spiritual sense, no matter how dearly paid for. It is the acceptance of one's one and only life cycle as something that had to be and that, by necessity, permitted of no substitutions. It thus means a new, a different love of one's parents. It is a comradeship with the ordering ways of distant times and different pursuits, as expressed in the simple products and sayings of such times and pursuits. Although aware of the relativity of all the various life styles which have given meaning to human striving, the possessor of integrity is ready to defend the dignity of his own life style against all physical and economical threats. For he knows that an individual life is the accidental coincidence of but one life cycle with but one segment of history; and that for him all human integrity stands or falls with the one style of integrity of which he partakes. The style of integrity developed by his culture of civilization, thus becomes the "patrimony of his soul," the seal of his moral paternity of himself. (*Childhood and Society*, p. 268.)

The chronic schizophrenic patient, too, in his progress toward increased adaptive capacity and independence, approximates this final step of development. He too feels the need to do for others. Frequently beginnings of this stage appear in the psychotherapeutic transaction. For example, the patient may begin to bring small presents to the therapist or to do small favors. He may bring coffee to the psychotherapy hour, or he may remember the therapist's favorite cigar; not infrequently he may bring things he has made, such as Christmas cards, paintings, poems, or ceramics. He may offer to do favors for the therapist, such as mailing letters, doing errands, or driving the therapist to the airport on his next trip. All of these offers of doing for the therapist should be seen as moves in the direction of increased independence; in fact, of developing dependency gratification by doing for the important others. To handle these presents, these favors, by the usual psychoanalytic technique of exploring them in detail for the aspect of the motivation for the gift that includes seduction, bribe, and so forth can be destructive to the patient. These elements probably do exist in the gifts and the favors, but they are minor compared to the positive step that they represent in the direction of the patient's being able to do for others rather than having others constantly do for him. If the therapist can handle the presents and favors appropriately and therapeutically by accepting them and pointing to their meaning in terms of the patient's growth and development, the patient may be able to move even further and begin to do for others outside of the psychotherapeutic transaction. In a hospital ward, he may be able to help other patients. (In some treatment centers ex-patients have been used effectively as auxiliary therapists and attendants.) Patients who have families of their own, including children, can be helped to obtain pleasure from the development and growth of their children. Other patients can obtain similar satisfaction from living less constricted lives. They can participate in community affairs, doing volunteer work in which they have an opportunity to do for and to give to others. It must be remembered that even in this state of remission, the chronic schizophrenic patient maintains his basic defect of not being able to trust entirely any fellow human being. He cares for others; he allows others to develop some dependence on him, but always with reservations, always somewhat on guard, always ready to demonstrate that others are unreliable and untrustworthy. Much of his caring for others maintains an "as if" quality—as if he were concerned about others, he cares for them, and he allows them to depend on him. Such a façade must be supported by the therapist, and, if held long enough, it may become firmly integrated among the many façades with which the patient covers his emptiness, his loneliness, and his disorganization.

The problem of terminating therapy is discussed in detail in Chapter 6. Perhaps the most important generalization we can make to the therapist caring for the chronic schizophrenic patient is to say, "Don't be in a hurry." Even long after the patient has maintained an excellent remission and appears to be using the therapeutic transaction rarely and relying on the therapist only a very little, the therapist remains an important prop in the maintenance of a comfortable and adaptive homeostasis. Even when the patient uses the therapist only once every three or six months, or even by phone only once a year, the maintenance of the therapeutic transaction as insurance of the possibility of care may make the difference between adequate functioning and the need for rehospitalization. A number of studies have shown that keeping patients on the roster of an aftercare facility serves a useful therapeutic function. When such patients were notified by letter that their cases were being closed, even after they had not had contact with the facility for over a year, they frequently responded by developing exacerbation of symptoms or by making contact for further treatment. Our basic thesis in the care of the chronically ill is the need for very long-term support, which may not require much active intervention but which may necessitate many years'—if not lifelong—maintenance of the relationship.

If the dependency in the psychotherapeutic transaction is precisely monitored and appropriately managed, the patient may use this relationship as a new prototype for other human relationships. The long-term supportive therapeutic relationship may replace the old defective prototype and may allow the patient to form relationships with other human beings that offer him some support, some safe gratification of dependency, and a springboard from which to make bolder attempts at relating and trusting.

5

Countertransference Problems

It is small wonder that the large, untreated population of chronically mentally ill patients suffer from neglect and lack of interest in the areas of both research and treatment. It is difficult to find therapists who are willing to devote a large measure of time, energy, and personal investment to the treatment and care of chronic patients—especially chronically mentally ill patients—since the amount of gratification appears, at least superficially, to be limited. The limitation of gratification for the physician or therapist who cares for the chronic patient is built into the transaction, in that he is, in fact, involved in long-term treatment of an illness that may have a slowly progressive downhill course. No matter how much the individual therapist recognizes in theory the chronic patient's need for treatment, it is difficult to maintain gratification when he finds himself in the position of administering treatment in a situation leading to such a course. Just as Churchill did not wish to be Prime Minister to preside over the dissolution of the British Empire, so the physician does not wish to be in the position of presiding over a slowly progressive dissolution of human functioning. Although it is said by some specialists, such as the family physician, that much gratification can be obtained from contact with individuals for many years and through many illnesses, the follow-up of these chronic cases frequently reveals to us that we have not been nearly as good therapists as we had wanted to be. It is easy for the surgeon who intervenes acutely to feel well satisfied with his work, especially if he leaves the postoperative follow-up to a specialist in internal medicine. Then he never has to face the serious question of efficacy of treatment when it is discovered that a patient on whom a duodenal resection for ulcer pain was performed has, in fact, two or three years later more problems and more symptoms than he did prior to surgery.

Public health physicians have long known that one of the serious limitations of gratification in their field is the difficulty of knowing exactly what one has prevented. Similarly, in the care of the chronically ill it is difficult to feel firmly and securely convinced of the worth-whileness of an effort at preventing secondary complications of chronic emotional illness when one cannot, in fact, test what one has prevented. Statistically, the question can be approached in terms of comparing treated to untreated patients, but this test is of little help in the individual case. One might well feel satisfied with the long-term results of treating a chronic schizophrenic patient and, in fact, be willing to take credit for the continued high level of the patient's functioning. One can obtain such gratification by comparing the level of functioning of this patient to other patients one has known who have not been treated. There is always the gnawing doubt, however, that had this patient not been treated, perhaps he still would not have shown a decline of functioning and perhaps the natural history of this particular illness, in this particular patient of this particular time, would have followed exactly the same course without treatment as it did with treatment.

Another limitation on the amount of gratification one can obtain from caring for and treating the chronically ill is the constant living example the patient represents of one's failures and limits of knowledge. Regular contact with the chronically ill patient reminds us vividly of all of the limitations of our science and art. It constantly reminds us of our inability to fulfill both the patient's and our own wishes for omnipotence and omniscience. The treatment of such a patient demonstrates to us the essence of human helplessness in the face of nature and disease.

In the care of the chronically ill, the young therapist is often humiliated and frustrated to find how useless is most of what he has learned about the dynamics and treatment of illness. Thus, the physician has to face failure, frustration, therapeutic impotence, and frequently loss of control over the course of the illness. How does he react to these feelings, and how do these reactions manifest themselves in behavior in the therapeutic transaction with the patient? In this chapter we shall try to look at these reactions and their manifestations, with the view that a therapist who is forewarned will be better able to monitor the countertransference and to keep out of the therapeutic transaction the part that would be anti-therapeutic for the patient.

One of the most common reactions to therapeutic frustration and confusion is to resort to magical intervention. When we as therapists do not understand the nature of the transaction with the patient or the part of the transaction that is therapeutic, we tend to ascribe the results to specific interventions that fit our theoretical model. If we are pharmacologically oriented, we tend to believe that the pharmacological effect of the pill is what brings about the desired effect. If we are psychoanalytically oriented, we tend to believe that the interpretation brings about the desired change in the patient. Unfortunately, a magical approach tends to be self-validating, so that the magic cannot be counteracted by observation. As a result of such a belief in magic on the part of the physician (the patient also may believe in the magical power of the physician, and indeed a good physician uses such a belief to benefit the patient), many patients have been given harmful and expensive treatment that was of very limited efficacy. For example, a chronic schizophrenic patient who responds to the therapist's concern, interest, and attention will participate with the psychoanalytically-oriented psychotherapist in the exploration of unconscious processes and the acceptance of interpretations as the price he pays for this attention, concern, and interest. He may well spend 45 minutes, three times a week, in this process, when, indeed, the same end could be accomplished in ten minutes, once a week. But since the therapist needs to validate his theory and to practice in a way in which he has been trained to practice, the patient will participate in the transaction on the therapist's terms for the attention, concern, and interest that he needs and that could be given to him more economically and effectively. If the therapist believes in the magic of pharmacological agents, the patient may take pills to the point of toxicity and severe side effects involving much physical suffering, because that is the price he must pay for attention, concern, and interest. The pharmacologically-oriented therapist must for his own needs give pills and must practice in the therapeutic transaction consistently with his theory of disease and treatment. If he complicates the impairment of the patient by drugging him, making him toxic, and decreasing his already tenuous hold on reality, the patient will go along as the price that he pays for the therapist's concern. The history of medicine is full of horror stories of the excesses that we, as physicians, have practiced on our patients. The bloodletting, the poisonings, the surgical mutilations, and the lobotomies bear witness not only to the ignorance of physicians, but also to the tremendous price patients are willing to pay in order to obtain the benevolent attention of someone who is endowed by them with the powers of healing and the relief of suffering.

The young therapist who has been trained within the

framework of the acute intervention in a crisis-style illness frequently responds to the frustration of caring for the chronically ill by becoming angry at the patient for his failure to respond. The patient who does not get well is perhaps the most painful reminder of our therapeutic impotence. Some therapists respond with humility, which, indeed, may be excessive and lead to a kind of therapeutic nihilism. Others respond with anger; this anger may be at the patient, at society, at the powers that be, or at himself. When it is expressed toward the patient, frequently the therapeutic intent of the transaction is abrogated, for the patient recognizes that the therapist is angry. An angry therapist has little chance of succeeding with the chronically ill patient, even when an attitude of firmness and brusqueness is indicated as a therapeutic intervention. As soon as the attitude is an expression of the angry feelings of the therapist rather than a planned, controlled therapeutic attitude, it becomes ineffective or even antitherapeutic. Usually the angry therapist unconsciously has a tendency to punish the patient, to trick him, and not infrequently to produce an exacerbation of symptoms. The angry therapist often becomes very demanding toward the patient, making demands upon him that he cannot possibly meet. The patient will participate in the demand schedule and will tend to get into situations that result in failure. The result is usually an exacerbation of symptoms and a fairly disastrous disorganization of the patient's life style. As an example of this result, one frequently sees a young therapist become discouraged and angered by the lack of progress of a patient who comes in each week to recite the same difficulties. He may then respond by saying to the patient, "I think you really ought to get a job. Why don't you go out and look for one?" At this point, the patient may look for a job but, being unable to function well enough to be hired, he will find it difficult to face the therapist for the next appointment. He will miss appointments, lose his support, and become further disorganized.

Chronically ill patients require long-term and frequently

rather massive emotional support from the therapist. This need and demand by the patient, which manifest themselves in many ways, evoke feelings in the therapist that may then lead to an alteration in his own behavior. Usually these demands are manifested by pleas for attention and time, behavioral calls for help and, on occasion, a kind of acting-out behavior against the therapist. The adequately trained therapist is usually able to handle such demands over a period of time. He can handle them repeatedly in crises, but with the chronic schizophrenic patient, for example, whose demands may go on for years and decades, the therapist finds it difficult not to feel exhausted and overtaxed in trying to meet them. In caring for the chronically ill, it is easy to demonstrate how much these patients depend on support from the therapist. When, for example, the therapist has certain personal stresses in his life he frequently notices that all of his patients seem to be getting upset. There are more phone calls, more crises, more suicide attempts. When he analyzes the situation, he discovers that the patients are responding to the fact that he has more energy invested in his own problem-solving and therefore less available for his patients. Since these patients are so ill and so empty, they cannot tolerate even a temporary withdrawal of energy by the therapist, and precisely at this point they make more demands. The therapist who is already being taxed by the demands of his own personal situation is then further taxed by increasing demands from his patients and may easily respond with antitherapeutic rage and rejection toward them. We have seen many situations where the therapist feels like saying to the chronic patient who is threatening suicide, "Why don't you go ahead and do it and solve my problems that way?" Of course, he would not make this remark to a patient, but the feeling can be conveyed without its ever having been expressed verbally. Once the patient picks up such an attitude, the results are usually disastrous for the patient, and the guilt produced in the therapist is of no value in helping him to be more effective with his patients.

It is therefore important that the therapist not overextend himself to his patients nor do things nor promise to do things that he cannot continue to do over a long period of time. Chronic patients do not tolerate very well a fluctuating level of giving by the therapist. The therapist is well advised if he gives only as much attention, concern, interest, and time to his chronic patients as he is prepared to expend over a long period of time.

Among the therapist's problems in treating a large number of chronic patients over a long period of time are boredom and loss of interest. Since very little "happens" (except during crises) in these treatment interactions, the therapist may fall into the position of listening without hearing. He may be bored with hearing, hour after hour, day after day, the same stories, the same laments, the same dull details. Although he appears attentive on the surface, he is not really listening; he is no longer engaged with the patient. When this situation occurs, the therapeutic transaction is in serious danger. First, the lack of interest and concern is conveyed to the patient, who responds by becoming less functional and less able to use the therapeutic encounter. Second, the therapist then begins to miss important clues that would help him to monitor the patient's life in such a way as to minimize complications and to maximize functioning. It is for this reason that an occasional change of therapist every few years for the chronic patient may not only not interfere with treatment but, indeed, may help the situation. It is also for this reason that the therapist should be careful to accept patients for long-term supportive care only when they interest him in some way that can sustain his engagement for a long period of time. A highly experienced but tired, bored, and somewhat inattentive therapist may not do the patient as much good as an inexperienced, untrained therapist, who is discovering with the patient anew and afresh what it is like to live in the world as a schizophrenic. If the therapist finds his interest lagging, almost any device that he can use to rekindle it will help the patient. Some therapists manage to care for the chronically ill because of their interest in research. Others continue to care for these patients in order to understand more about illness, which will allow them exercises in theory building. In fact, it has been observed that well-trained senior members of the profession who continue to care for chronic and very ill schizophrenic patients are usually involved in research, teaching, or theory-building. Therapists who are primarily interested in treatment tend to avoid chronically ill patients after some exposure to them, and to concentrate on the more acute situation where the time-span of a therapeutic endeavor is more limited.

Caring for the chronically mentally ill patient involves therapeutic problems for the therapist in the area of expecta-tion. The patient's hope, wish, and expectancy for the future are important aspects of the treatment situation. Very early in the therapeutic engagement, the therapist reinforces this attitude and, indeed, helps the patient to see that life can be different, that the future does not have to be like the past, and that choices are available to him. As the years roll by in the treatment of the chronic patient, the therapist may find it harder and harder to keep the future open with hope. The patient usually is not nearly so concerned about the passage of time as is the therapist. The therapist may respond to his own uneasiness about the future with feelings of being a fraud, of having promised more than he can deliver. Such a feeling on the therapist's part occurs, however, only when he mis-understands the real function of hope in the therapeutic trans-action. The function of hope is to pull the patient into the future. Such a pull allows the patient to continue to exist and thus to be exposed to new experiences that can bring about some changes, it is hoped for the better, and it allows him to utilize those resources that are undamaged by illness.

As the therapist feels more fraudulent in not delivering the promised goods, however, he may unconsciously convey to the patient his anxiety and frustration. Frequently, at this point, the therapeutic relationship is interrupted or indeed severed, usually with a fairly disastrous result for the patient.

Actually, patients of the type discussed in this book find it relatively easy to change therapists. Their relationships are generally diffused to the helping situation rather than concentrated specifically on one helping individual. This observation makes it easier to treat such patients, since they can be transferred from therapist to therapist, can be taken care of by others during vacations, and can even form relationships with the institution of the helping situation. Although in the specific treatment transaction the relationship may seem specific and intense with one principal therapist, response to his absence is frequently minimal if adequate alternative support is provided. Recognition of this fact can be painful for the therapist. Typically, he will discover that he is more involved with his patients personally than his patients are with him. He will discover that during vacations he misses them more than they do him, and that they get along quite well while being seen by someone else. Unless the therapist understands this fact and is prepared for it, he may respond to this apparent rejection by his patients with anger and rejection of them. There is also a risk that the therapist may be seduced by his patients' statements (*e.g.,* that he is the only doctor who has ever understood them, or that he is the best doctor in the world) into believing in his own omnipotence.

Having listed the many problems which confront the therapist in taking care of chronically and severely mentally ill patients over a long period of time, let us list some gratifications that he may expect. First of all, the therapist may obtain much gratification from the feeling of meeting a huge unmet need that few of his colleagues are willing to meet. Second, he will usually see behavioral changes in patients very quickly. This result is one of the paradoxes of the situation. With a chronically ill schizophrenic, one hour a month of treatment may result in major behavioral changes, whereas one hour a month of treatment with a neurotic patient would produce no change. In fact, if one thinks in these terms, it becomes obvious that one hour a month over a period of twenty years may well keep a chronic schizophrenic patient working and functioning, and sometimes even allow him to make a creative contribution to the world—all for 240 hours. Yet we know that 240 hours of intensive psychoanalytic treatment of a neurotic patient is only the beginning of the time commitment necessary to bring about changes in behavior. In these terms, then, the care of the chronically ill actually delivers more "miles per gallon" to the therapist than the treatment of the less chronically and less severely ill. Many of these patients, in spite of being ill, have many areas of strength and health. Some of them can become sources of a kind of relationship that can be gratifying to the therapist, the kind of relationship that general practitioners talk about when they think of their long-term contacts with families. There are other gratifications in the treatment of the chronically emotionally ill. These patients usually are loyal. They will continue to be a therapist's patient until the therapist dismisses them. They will keep their appointments, they will pay their bills regularly, and they generally know how to be "good" patients. They usually do not express much open hostility to the therapist and have a tendency to idealize him.

A therapist who understands the problems of treating the chronically mentally ill and who is willing to engage in such treatment interactions will never have a shortage of patients. He will be a busy, well-paid practitioner with many grateful patients who have feelings of loyalty and respect for him and who function better because of his skill and understanding.

Part **II**

PRACTICE

6

Beginning and Ending

BEGINNING

Once a patient has been diagnosed as having a chronic mental illness that requires supportive care as the treatment of choice, the therapist faces the task of beginning the treatment transaction. We have mentioned that treatment starts, in fact, long before the patient and the therapist actually meet. It may begin when the patient identifies himself as being in need of concern and care, or when he seeks help from various facilities—when he looks for emotional support from medical and nonmedical sources. Our concern here, however, is to deal with the technical problems of beginning the treatment transaction with the patient once he has been identified as being in need of care.

The therapist may be confronted with the problem of getting the patient to come in for an appointment. He may have been contacted by a referring physician or by the family, and he may have surmised from the history given him that, indeed, this is a patient who seems to be suffering from a chronic mental illness and needs to be seen. If the patient is not willing to come in, the question then is what the therapist can do to promote a willingness, in order to be able to assess the patient. A common error made by therapists is to take a nondirective attitude and to justify this approach by a carica-ture of psychoanalytic technique. It is true that with an intact, healthy neurotic patient it is appropriate to let treatment begin on the basis of the patient's strong, positive motivation for change. It is appropriate with such patients and in such situations to take the stand that whether or not the patient receives treatment is entirely up to him—that the choice is his. In the patient population with which we are concerned in this book, however, such a beginning is inappropriate. With such a patient, the physician must take a strong stand that the patient is in need of treatment and that he should come in for an appointment. The recommendation may include the assurance that the physician will "go after" the patient in every possible way. Frequently, the chronically mentally ill patient will express his feelings of hopelessness, alienation, worthless-ness, and panic by his reluctance to become involved in any kind of relationship with anyone, including a potential psycho-therapist. Such a patient may come to feel that someone cares or is really concerned about him, that someone considers him worth while, only after the therapist has taken a strong stand by insisting that the patient needs to be seen, to be evaluated, and to be treated. It is necessary that the therapist be in-terested enough to insist that the patient do so. With such patients, the therapist takes at the beginning the more traditional stance of the physician who has a point of view about treatment, who makes a recommendation, who places pressure on the patient for compliance in the medical trans-action, and who conveys to the patient that he, the physician, will do whatever is necessary and proper to insure that the patient receive the appropriate treatment.

The psychotherapist may find it necessary to be even firmer than the traditional physician in insisting on treatment. Not infrequently, the chronically mentally ill patient is so caught up in his closed future and his fears of involvement that he cannot accept the very much desired invitation to engage in a relationship with someone who offers support and care. It is for this reason that legal measures must be used at times to exert pressure on the patient to engage in such a relationship. Although in most states the law is to be used to give treatment to the patient who is "dangerous to himself and others," very few patients fall into this category. Most states' laws, however, allow the use of legal pressure when the patient is in need of "treatment and care." This possibility by no means implies that patients should be legally committed if they are reluctant to begin the treatment transaction with the psychotherapist, or if their ambivalence and feelings of alienation and worthlessness keep them from becoming involved with a supportive therapist. What we mean is that the therapist should take as strong a stand as is necessary and should not leave it to the patient to demonstrate the motivated behavior that we require in expressive psychotherapy. Some therapists may even go so far as to say to a new patient on the telephone, "After discussing some of the problems with your family doctor and with your husband, I think it is very important for you to come in to see me, so that you and I can discover how I can be of help. I want you to come in for an appointment on Thursday, December 3, and I insist that you and I get together to give you this help." Very few patients will refuse such a positive approach. On rare occasions it may be necessary to go further, even to the extent of indicating to the patient that the therapist will take whatever steps are necessary, including the initiation of involuntary procedures, to get the patient involved and to keep him coming for treatment.

Generally, once the patient has been seen for the first

appointment, there is relatively little difficulty in getting him to continue to come. Most of the patients who require supportive care are so hungry for help and concern that they have little difficulty accepting them when they are appropriately offered. Some patients may test the situation. They may do so by raising many and varied objections to treatment, or by not showing up for a return appointment. The objections to being involved with treatment need to be dealt with, both realistically and also in terms of their meaning as a form of fear of involvement. If, for example, the patient states that he cannot afford the fee for treatment, and if this question has been evaluated by the therapist and found to be a realistic problem, it is the therapist's task to refer the patient to a source of supportive care where the fee is less of a problem. He must do more, however, than simply give the name of an agency to such a patient. He must concern himself with getting the patient there, even to the extent of calling the agency, arranging an appointment for the patient, and demonstrating interest and concern in getting the patient to keep the appointment. His concern should include a follow-up telephone call to see whether the patient kept the appointment. If, on the other hand, the patient raises a question about money as an expression of his guilt or reluctance in becoming involved in supportive care, and if this attitude is not realistic, then the situation must be handled in a direct manner. To interpret reluctance to engage in treatment as manifested in a concern about money simply as a resistance or as an aspect of feelings of worthlessness will be ineffective with the patients of whom we are speaking here. Even though one might proceed thus with a neurotic patient who required expressive psychotherapy, to do so with the chronic psychotic patient will result in his not returning for the supportive care that he needs. Rather, the therapist must adopt a positive stance, and he might deal with the patient as follows: "I wonder if your concern about the fee isn't out of proportion. I think you are too involved in your troubles to be objective about it, and I think it will be of help if I have a talk with someone in your family about it. Meanwhile, you come again to see me for your next appointment, and the matter of the fee will be worked out." Much of the time the unrealistic concern about money, as well as the patient's reluctance to become involved in the treatment process, is simply his way of testing whether the therapist is really concerned, really cares, and can really be relied on as a supporting figure.

As we have mentioned, many a patient comes to a therapist as the result of a family member's concern about him. When the bridge to treatment is the family, it is important for the therapist to make early contact with significant family members. Although it is important to keep the individual patient as the focus of the therapist's concern and, moreover, although it is important to clarify almost immediately the fact that the therapist is the agent for the patient rather than for the family, it is nevertheless vital that the family members have an opportunity to see the therapist early in the treatment. Frequently, on the first visit, we spend a portion of the time with one or more significant family members present for the interview with the patient. This procedure is important in order to help the therapist to assess the potential of the family members to serve as supporting figures, to assess the dynamics with which the patient has to live, and also to give the family an opportunity to meet the therapist in person. Such a meeting helps to minimize the distortions that will go on in the future as the patient reports his contacts with the therapist to the family. For the therapist to be firm and to insist on continuation of the appointments, for him to see members of the family, and for him to express his conviction of the patient's need for supportive care, can all serve to reassure the patient that someone is indeed concerned and that someone does care about his difficulties.

The frequency of visits during the early stages of treatment is a question that must be considered. As we have said, regularity of visits is an essential of supportive care for a chronically mentally ill patient. We have also stated that visits that are too frequent or too long can be interpreted by the patient as a demand for a closeness and a level of functioning that he cannot meet, thus resulting in a negative therapeutic effect. At the beginning of treatment, although there may be a great deal of pressure from the family and from the patient for frequent visits during the evaluation, the therapist should be cautious in considering all facets of the decision about frequency. He must consider, for example, the pattern that he is setting if he sees a patient three or four times a week for the first few weeks during the evaluation period, only to decide thereafter on once-a-week visits for supportive care. Will he then have to deal with what the patient considers to be a rejection? Will his evaluation be distorted by the patient's fear of involvement in a situation that seems to demand more closeness than the patient can manage? Will a pattern be set for treatment that the patient will find difficult to give up? All of these and other considerations should make the therapist cautious about seeing patients more frequently than once a week. It is true that at the beginning of treatment a patient may need more reassurance—perhaps even more contacts— than a once-a-week visit will provide. Much of this problem, however, can be handled by alternative methods. For example, the patient may be encouraged to call the therapist once a day to report his symptoms, or he may be encouraged to keep track of certain symptoms in writing until the next appointment one week later. To begin the treatment by setting a pattern of weekly appointments and to convey to the patient the attitude of regularity, lack of panic, and certainty about the appropriate course to follow can be a tremendous reassurance in the initial phase of supportive care.

The therapist must be careful to evaluate all of the patient's behavior in a therapeutic context. For example, for the patient to demand more frequent visits may again be a testing situation. The issue may not be frequency of visits but rather control of the patient's need to test the therapist, to evaluate what demands will be made on him to overextend himself beyond his capacity, or to express his readiness or reluctance to become involved. For all of these and other aspects of communication, the therapist must keep his ear tuned and then respond appropriately. With a neurotic patient the therapist would tend to take these communications out of the metaphor and to confront the patient with a decoded direct message. With a chronically ill patient, it is best for the therapist to remain within the metaphor and to respond to the patient's latent communication by utilizing his own metaphor. For example, if a patient responds to being told that he will be seen once a week for the next few weeks to evaluate his need for treatment by saying "I'd be glad to come more often if you can find the time to see me," the therapist must choose how to respond. If he were dealing with a neurotic or personality-disorder patient, he might well make an immediate confrontation: "It seems to me that you are asking how interested I really am in you and how much I'm willing to give to you." With the chronically ill patient, however, it is far better to leave the communication in the metaphor and to respond: "I think it would be excellent to come in more frequently if I needed to see you more often. However, I've found that I can learn the most about you most rapidly and can be of the most help if I see you once a week. Of course, I want you to know that if something comes up that you are very much concerned about or if you wish to talk to me, you can always pick up the telephone and call, and we can always then make the decision whether you need an extra appointment." By responding in the metaphor, the patient is told that the therapist recognizes the nature of the communication, that he can understand, and that he is certain about the course of action to be taken. The therapist should further communicate that he is in control of the treatment and that the patient is not to try to treat himself. In order to demonstrate this necessity, we insist that the patient make no changes in his medication or plan of living without first discussing it with the therapist and obtaining his approval.

At the beginning patients often spend a great deal of time

testing the safety of the therapeutic relationship with a new supportive therapist. In the medical setting, most frequently they do so by talking about other doctors whom they have consulted. In a disguised, latent way they are evaluating the therapist. They may begin the treatment transaction by complaining about other physicians whom they have seen. It is important for the therapist to recognize the latent meaning of this communication and not to fall into the trap of agreeing with the patient, even if the patient has been seen by someone who seems quite incompetent and who has not done an especially good job of handling the patient's needs. For the new therapist to agree with the patient's criticism of another therapist would be disastrous for the new therapeutic relationship. This statement does not mean that the new therapist has to defend whatever others have done. What it does mean is that the therapist must recognize that whenever the patient talks about other physicians, the patient is also at the same time evaluating and talking about the new therapist. For example, metaphorically, the patient asks the new therapist with whom he is beginning supportive care whether he can rely on him by stating: "My general practitioner is always so busy. When I've called him in the past, sometimes it has taken three days to get him to return the call; but then I can understand that. After all, he has to deliver babies and so on." By ignoring the statement or by agreeing with the patient, the therapist is immediately sabotaging the supportive care situation. If, on the other hand, the therapist recognizes that the patient is testing and can respond by saying: "I guess it was very difficult for you not to be able to talk to someone when you needed to, but I want you to know that when you call me I'll make every effort to return the call, and I will be able to do so," he can use the metaphor to reassure the patient within the safety of the disguised communication.

Essentially, then, the techniques of beginning the treatment of chronic patients who suffer from psychotic illnesses require an active intervention by the therapist in which he demonstrates his concern for and interest in the patient and in which he is willing to be directive and to take over for the patient's defective adaptive capacity. He must function in the role of a "doctor," in which he prescribes, gives advice, insists on the patient's compliance with the treatment plan, and involves the family. At the same time the therapist must be sensitive to the many disguised and tentative signals that the patient sends to test him, to see whether he really does care about the patient in his difficulty. The therapist must be sensitive to these tests and must, usually within the metaphor, respond to them by reassuring the patient that he can expect care consistently and that he can rely on it during the period of time that he needs to have support.

ENDING

Repeatedly in this book we have made the point that supportive care essentially never ends. We have discussed how the supportive relationship must continue throughout the life of the patient and the therapist. This somewhat disquieting statement does not mean, however, that formal psychotherapeutic relationships cannot and should not end, nor does it imply that there cannot be certain shifts throughout the patient's life in the sources of his support. We have also mentioned the need that the therapist not be in a hurry. This point must be emphasized repeatedly. Supportive care is a long-term process, which, when successful, results in a major retraining of the patient. This retraining involves the development of trust, which then permits the patient to reach out to others for support and to give up some of his dependence on the therapist and on formal psychotherapeutic intervention. Thus, in spite of the fact that supportive care involves a nonending process, it is necessary to consider the factors involved in changing the sources of support in the patient's life.

When the patient has developed security in the relationship with the therapist, when he has developed trust in the therapist as a fellow human being, and when this trust has expanded into a trust of the patient in himself and in his judgment and in his abilities (see Chapter 4), then it is possible to make some major shifts in the relationship with the therapist. Although we have emphasized that the therapist who engages in supportive care needs to understand the continuing nature of the relationship and that he must not be in a hurry—that he must not let his therapeutic zeal interfere with the patient's therapeutic needs—we have said little about the therapist's tendency to fail to recognize changes in the patient. A therapist may make the error of continuing to think of the patient as nonfunctioning and extremely ill, thus keeping him too dependent and too regressed and too infantilized. It is undeniable that therapists, like all parental figures, have a tendency not to keep up with changes in their patients and thus to see them as more dependent, more inadequate, and sicker than they really are. Such a failure on the part of the therapist may then result in an expectancy about the patient's behavior that does not maximize his functioning. As the patient improves, the therapist must change in giving the patient more responsibility and more opportunity to rely on his own judgment. He must also allow and appropriately encourage the patient to engage in relationships with others outside the psychotherapeutic situation, so that the patient may broaden the base of his relationships and the sources of his support.

One of the important changes that occurs in the psychotherapeutic transaction, as the patient develops improved judgment and reliance upon self and as the therapist recognizes this change and helps the patient to reach out to others, is that the therapist takes an active and assisting role in the patient's planning for life. He may help the patient to find a suitable job or to move in the direction of a suitable profession. He may guide the patient like a good parent in his relationships to others, in joining organizations, and perhaps even in finding a suitable fellow human being for marriage.

In this process of referring the patient to life he slowly moves from the position of being a therapist to being a supportive, parental friend. As he allows this change to occur, he continues to take an active part in the patient's life, and in taking this active part he continues to use the techniques earlier described as therapeutic in supportive care. That is to say, as the patient reaches out to others and reaches out to life, as he continues to grow and develop, as he is able to give up some of his dependence on the therapist, and as the therapist moves readily into the role of being a friendly, parental guide, the therapist still continues to help the patient to focus on activity, on reality, on keeping the future open, and on the development of trust in other human beings.

In all of these aspects, the therapist takes an assisting and active role, even to the extent of participating somewhat in the patient's outside life. For example, the therapist may even develop some social contacts with the patient by participating in certain activities, such as going to a graduation, a marriage, or a party. It is important to remember, however, that even in these settings the therapist must remain a therapist; that is to say, he must be available then and in the future for the patient to use him as a therapist. If he shifts entirely into the role of friend, which means that the relationship with the patient changes to one in which both the therapist and the patient are tempted to gain gratification from the other, then the patient loses the supporting role that he needs. The essence of the therapeutic relationship is that the patient comes to someone whose goal it is to treat him, and he comes with specific therapeutic needs that can be met. The therapist, on his part, comes to this relationship with specific needs to function as a therapist, and he finds his compensation in professional satisfaction and in financial rewards. This relationship is very different from the social relationship, in which two persons meet on an equal basis, each one attempting to receive an equal amount of gratification from the other and expecting to derive gratification from the contact.

Thus, even as the therapist refers the patient to life and

even as he becomes more active and more assisting in a friendly, paternal, supportive role, he must maintain himself in the role of a therapist in the sense mentioned above, that is to say, he does not expect the immediate and equal gratification from the relationship that he could expect from a friend. Even when the therapist attends a patient's social function, he must keep clearly in mind that he is a therapist and that the patient needs now and in the future to maintain him in that role. This necessity does not mean that he talks like a therapist or makes interpretations or confrontations while in the social situation. It means that he observes the situation, that he gives the support that the patient needs in the situation, and that afterward in an appointment the patient and the therapist can discuss what went on in that situation with a clinical focus in order to understand and expand the patient's reliance on himself.

As the therapist gradually shifts from the traditional role of supportive care to the new role, he may become more active in giving advice. His advice, however, is different from that of real parents or of social friends in that it is always based on a thorough knowledge of the patient's capacities, potentials, and limitations, and on his understanding of the psychopathological processes that he has seen in the patient in the past and that lie latent as the patient moves into a state of good remission. That does not mean that patients do not change. As we have mentioned, it is important that a therapist allow a patient to develop; but it is also important that he remember the patient's difficulties and weaknesses, in order to prevent their development once again. For example, the therapist and the patient together may decide that, although the patient can function well, he should not have children. They may recognize together that such a demand on his adaptive psychological processes would be overwhelming. Then it is the task of the therapist not only to help the patient to practice adequate contraception, but also to deal with his feelings of not fulfilling the aspect of life that involves parenthood. The therapist must help the patient to review his own wishes or fears about having a child and then to resolve this aspect in terms of the patient's needs, rather than in terms of society's expectations. Whether or not a patient who has required long-term supportive care should have a child depends entirely on the particular patient. As we mentioned in Chapter 4, some patients can obtain a great deal of growth and development and gratification from raising a child and can switch their dependency needs to the role of taking care of a child.

As the therapist engages in the shifting role that involves changing some of the aspects of supportive care, a number of problems will arise. For example, when the therapist visits the patient at various social functions, should he charge his usual fee? It is in this area that some changes can readily be made. For example, if the therapist visits the family or meets with the family of the patient early in treatment when the situation is formally and precisely defined as treatment, he should certainly charge his usual fee. He is then making a home visit or doing a home study, which is an important part of the treatment. If, however, during the "ending" phase of treatment he accepts a dinner invitation or attends a patient's party, the therapist can signal the social aspects of the relationship by not charging for the time spent with the patient. This signal may be important to the patient in showing him how far he has developed and grown, and how he can now find support from others on a broader base. The therapist, in his own mind at least, must nevertheless remain in the role of therapist even though he is not being paid. Usually, by the time supportive care has reached this stage, the therapist has so much invested in the patient and receives so much gratification from his own therapeutic success that payment is not necessary. Other problems may arise in this "ending" stage; for example, the patient may want to meet the therapist's family. In general, it is our feeling that his doing so is of very limited value and may be anti-therapeutic. If the patient is confronted by the reality of the therapist's private life, it may make it more difficult for him to maintain his fantasies about the therapist's life. These fantasies can be important in maintaining the therapist as a source of support. As an example of this problem, we once had a medical student who gave his home telephone number to a female patient whom he was seeing for supportive care. Frequently when the patient called, the student's wife would answer the telephone. The student would then come to the telephone and discuss with the patient whatever problem had motivated her call. This arrangement seemed to have an overall therapeutic effect for the patient until the student acceded to her request to meet the wife with whose voice she had become so well acquainted on the telephone. The result of this confrontation was that the therapist lost a great deal of therapeutic "leverage" with his patient, and the patient was no longer able to maintain her fantasy of the therapist as "belonging" to her in a special way. Her symptoms, which she had had under good control, promptly became more severe.

Although we speak in this section of our book about the ending of supportive care, it becomes obvious that in many subtle and rather complicated ways we do not end. We shift roles. We refer the patient to life; we encourage him to use the trust developed in the psychotherapeutic relationship by investing trust in others in his real life. We encourage him to use the relationship with the therapist as a prototype for other relationships; we decrease the number of actual contacts to an annual meeting or telephone call or Christmas card; but we never end in terms of planning never to meet again, never to see each other again, not to keep track of each other. Furthermore, we never really leave the role of being the psychotherapist. In all contacts in the future with this patient, we maintain certain important aspects of therapeutic function. Two persons who have a history of having transacted with each other as patient and therapist should not forget that history. For the patient who has a need for chronic supportive care, this history should not be forgotten, but rather a memory of it should remain an important source of support on which the patient can call in the future. Even in a healthy person, a memory of a happy, supportive relationship with parents can serve as a support throughout life.

Some of our readers may feel that we are proposing a dangerous policy of fostering chronic dependency. Nothing could be further from our intent, nor, in our view, from the effect of what we propose. We do recognize, however, the need on the part of these patients for a source of support that comes from the corrective emotional experience of having had a psychotherapeutic relationship. Our experience with chronically ill patients has brought us to an awareness that even with patients whom we have treated with more traditional expressive methods, a relationship has developed that really never ends. The positive transference continues, and indeed it should continue as a source of further growth and development throughout the life of the patient.

7

The Decision for Hospitalization

A period during which a patient's treatment is conducted in a hospital must be looked on as only a phase of the entire treatment. It is, however, an important phase. Indeed, in many instances the degree of appropriateness with which a person adopts the role of patient in the hospital critically determines the course of his illness and of the treatment intervention. Therapeutic use of the hospital may influence the success of the various phases of extramural management described in this book. The techniques of intramural care will be described in detail in the following chapter. Here we focus on the crucial factors leading to the decision for the prescription of hospitalization and also on the factors leading to the termination of hospitalization. It is in these areas that recent experiments with brief hospitalization and the newer conceptualization of crisis intervention as a form of definitive treatment have made it necessary for us to rethink and reformulate our views on the hospital as an agent of treatment.

Our present conceptual framework for considering hospitalization as an important—though brief—phase of treatment of the patient with chronic mental illness is a part of the major psychiatric revolution of our time. It is the largest leap forward in the treatment of psychotic patients since the introduction of hope in the form of chemical tranquilizers and the abolition of the practice of inflicting brain injury on the chronically mentally ill through various physical methods. We now recognize that much of the symptomatology as classically described in the chronic schizophrenic patient is in fact the result of chronic hospitalization rather than a disease process, and we now are able to view the treatment of such patients in terms of short periods of intramural care.

The question of inpatient treatment must allow discussion of (1) prescribing hospitalization; (2) experiences in the hospital—both therapeutic and antitherapeutic; (3) preparation for resumption of community living; (4) prescribing release from the hospital. It is, of course, arbitrary to regard these aspects separately, since the "before," the "during," and the "after" of hospitalization are importantly and meaningfully integrated as the patient lives them; but perhaps a separate discussion of these aspects will not do injustice to the reality of the situation, while at the same time making them accessible to study. In this chapter we shall consider item (1), prescribing hospitalization, and item (4), the decision for release from the hospital. In the following chapter we shall elaborate items (2) and (3), experiences in the hospital and preparation for resumption of community living.

The patient population under consideration suffers from an illness that is chronic and that displays exacerbations and remissions in its course. Just as we cannot identify with more than speculative confidence the relevant etiological variables of this illness, we are frequently at a loss to identify the precipitating events surrounding the exacerbation of its symptoms. Thus, even though we may have had a patient under long-term supportive care for some time, situations can occur in the patient-environment interaction that overtax the always tenuous adaptive capacities of the patient, and in these instances the question of hospitalization is frequently raised. In evaluating a new patient who appears for treatment for the first time by presenting himself in crisis to the doctor for help, a decision regarding hospitalization is necessary. Usually such direct questions as, "What caused the upset?" or "What's different about your life yesterday as compared with the last eight months?" will not lead to finding the specific pebbles over which the patient stumbled, thus upsetting the delicate homeostasis. On the other hand, an attempt to get a detailed history of the events that occurred twenty-four hours before the disruption of the homeostasis will frequently demonstrate apparently minor factors that upset the balance of adaptive capacities by which the patient was maintaining himself in the community. We have pointed out in Chapter 1 that the symptoms of the illness are best viewed as the final common path of many forces, including biological factors, psychological factors, social factors, economic factors, and so forth, all of which, coming together at a specific time, bring about the behavior that we call symptoms. The more of these factors that we can identify, the more intelligently we can intervene therapeutically in a multidimensional way. Similarly, the more factors we know in each of these categories that have supported the previous homeostasis of the chronic patient and that have now been altered in bringing about the present exacerbation of symptoms, the more intelligently we can prescribe hospitalization.

As a general principle we now recognize many of the untoward side effects of hospitalization, especially of prolonged hospitalization. These side effects include such factors as the further alienation of the patient from society, the reification of the patient's failure in his adaptive task, the reinforcement of the passive role toward the solution of his problems, the mobilization of the patient's remaining resources to adapt himself to the artificial society of the hospital rather than utilizing his resources for the task of adapting to the real society outside of the hospital, and the secondary guilt produced by supporting the patient's abandonment of his adaptive tasks in life. It is for these reasons that hospitalization should be prescribed only when there are specific indications for it, rather than when the therapist does not know what else to do. It is also for these reasons that hospitalization should be prescribed for the briefest possible period in order to accomplish the specific aims that are part of the treatment goal. The prevailing view of psychiatric hospitalization has been contaminated by the erroneous idea that any patient who required rehospitalization at some later date was probably not hospitalized long enough the first time. Nothing could be further from the truth. In the management of chronic mental illness, as well as in the management of chronic physical illness, repeated hospitalization may be indicated. To confuse the need for repeated hospitalization with the prescription of continued hospitalization has produced the iatrogenic emotional cripples who fill our state hospitals. Hospitalization is a potent treatment that can be potentially life-saving, but like any other potent treatment it can also be potentially disastrous to the patient. The proper use of hospitalization, taking into account all of the possible benefits and possible dangers, is a central part of the program in the management of patients with chronic illness.

Assuming for the moment that excellent facilities for hospital treatment are available, let us look at the criteria upon which one should base a judgment to prescribe hospitalization.

1. Is the patient's present condition so disturbed that he is unable to maintain the relationship with the therapist that is necessary for the outpatient management of the period of exacerbation? Here, such factors must be considered as: his ability to keep his appointments, to maintain himself between

appointments at an acceptable level of functioning, and to care for his social and biological needs, or at least to mobilize enough aid from significant others to have these needs met.

2. Is the patient's impulse control so tenuous that he and other significant figures in his life are too fearful to tolerate attempts to manage the exacerbation on an outpatient basis? If so, hospitalization is necessary in order to demonstrate control and thus to relieve the patient of the anxiety produced by his doubts about his own control.

3. Has the patient by his disturbed behavior alienated himself from the organizing and supportive resources formerly available to him, such as his job, his family, community agencies, and so forth? If these resources withdraw their support because they are no longer willing or able to tolerate his disturbance and his demands, then the homeostasis is quickly upset and the patient is in need of finding other support to which his disturbed behavior is more acceptable. One such support, of course, is the hospital. This very reason for hospitalization, however, is also one of the important disadvantages of hospital treatment. In general, unless very carefully supervised, hospitals tend to reinforce and support sick behavior rather than healthy behavior, and to that extent they tend to be antitherapeutic. On occasion brief hospitalization (by brief hospitalization we mean several days of hospitalization) may prevent a permanent alienation of the helping resources that were formerly mobilized by the patient.

4. Has the patient utilized pathological behavior in an attempt to cope with his exacerbation (excessive use of alcohol or drugs, malnutrition, and so on) to such an extent that hospital treatment is now necessary to correct its secondary results? A brief period of hospitalization to intervene in the aspects of the pathology that are the secondary and tertiary effects of the illness frequently can re-establish a much higher level of homeostasis that will allow the patient to function successfully extramurally.

5. Has there been a loss of a major source of support,

through death or other circumstances not brought about by the patient, on which his continuing functioning has relied? One should remember, however, in considering this factor that hospitalization is by no means the only alternative. On occasion it is necessary to hospitalize a patient for this reason, especially for the few days that it may take to mobilize other sources of support. We have found it useful to consider hospitalization for periods of even less than 24 hours in dealing with this factor. For example, let us say that a very ill chronic schizophrenic patient has maintained himself in a delicate homeostatic adaptive capacity, including a borderline functioning, by living with his aged mother. The mother becomes physically ill and needs to be hospitalized. At this point, the patient has lost his support and is unable to continue functioning. It is then useful to consider the possibility of hospitalizing the patient for a very brief period until contact can be made with some other significant person who will allow the patient to stay with him or who can come to stay with the patient while the mother is hospitalized or until some other solution has been found. Brief hospitalizations in moments of crisis during the treatment of chronic patients and a flexible approach to the use of hospitalization can prevent many of the secondary complications of chronic illness.

6. Does the patient need to be protected from self-destruction or from hurting others? Of course, this use of hospitalization is traditional. When a patient cannot be prevented from committing suicide or from inflicting harm on others, hospitalization is necessary as a measure of control; but this solution is too readily reached for. As we shall discuss in Chapter 13 on the treatment of the suicidal patient, there are other and better methods of preventing a patient from committing suicide than placing him in the hospital. Similarly, the potential danger to others is frequently overestimated by the physician. These are difficult decisions to make and must be based on such considerations as the patient's history of impulse control, the number of supporting and controlling fac-

tors available to him in the environment, the readiness with which he is able to use a human relationship as a helping situation, and the chronicity of the danger of self-destruction or of hurting others. Although protection is a valid reason for hospitalization, it is an indication that has been too broadly applied.

7. Is the patient in need of being protected from the possible consequences of his actions? A patient who, during exacerbations of illness or during psychotic episodes, behaves in a way that will in the future change his life situation may require hospitalization as a brief intervention. For example, a patient who during an exacerbation behaves in business in such a way that he will lose his customers or dissipate his resources should be protected from these actions, so that he will not at the time of remission face the additional burden of rebuilding from scratch. A patient who endangers his associations, friendships, business contacts, and professional relationships during a brief period of exacerbation might well be considered for hospitalization to prevent the secondary complications of the rupture of these relationships. If, of course, the alienation in associations is the result of his chronic maladaptive behavior, hospitalization will not intervene significantly in his life course, and he will have to find a new group of associates who are willing to tolerate his pathology. This alternative is preferable to chronic, prolonged hospitalization.

8. Does the patient need hospitalization at this time in the course of the management of his illness to reinforce the therapeutic intent? On occasion, especially at the beginning of treatment, it is necessary to hospitalize a patient in order to establish the relationship with the helping situation and to aid in the establishment of the patient's role. Nevertheless, the therapist must be careful in using hospitalization in this way so that chronicity is not produced by the kind of patient role that is established for the sick person. For some patients an occasional brief rehospitalization serves almost the func-

tion of a battery recharge. They view the hospital as the great stone mother, as the one steadfast, unchanging representation of the helping situation. They use the idea of the hospital and the visual image of the hospital as the helping situation; some of them drive by the hospital or telephone the hospital to reinforce the therapeutic intent. Then, every once in a while, this image fades and needs to be reinforced. At such times a readmission for several days may be necessary. In this brief rehospitalization the patient learns again that the hospital is always there; that it represents help, that it is populated by other representatives of the helping situation, and that aid is available. There are many patients who can manage with three or four days of hospitalization once a year for indefinite periods of time. In the older era of psychiatric treatment such patients would have been hospitalized for 20 or 30 years, becoming increasingly malfunctional and dependent, and demonstrating all of the symptoms of "chronic schizophrenia," which indeed are symptoms of chronic hospitalization. Hospitalization, of course, also provides gratification of dependency. This variable must be carefully monitored and fitted to the specific needs of each patient, as we shall discuss in considerable detail in Chapter 8 on hospital treatment.

9. Do the regularly available supportive resources need a brief vacation from the patient? This approach to the use of hospitalization has been successfully utilized in England in the care of geriatric patients. There are many families who can tolerate a very sick member in their midst if they are given the opportunity of occasional vacations. In the long-term management of such patients, it seems to us that an appropriate indication for brief hospitalization includes allowing the supportive resources the opportunity to gather new strength to deal with the patient.

10. At this time, is the patient in need of training in healthy behavior? Many chronic patients need help in adopting a new "as if" role in which a more appropriate adaptive façade is developed. On occasion the hospital is the best place

in which to retrain patients in healthy behavior. Of course, it is crucial that the hospital function well in its carefully planned treatment program. Many hospitals present a dangerous situation in which patients learn unhealthy behavior rather than healthy behavior.

11. Is the patient in need of the interruption of his isolation, and is the hospital the only place where it can be done? We mention in Chapter 13 that one of the most important aspects is the interruption of social isolation. Similarly, the increasing alienation from others frequently seen in chronic patients tends to snowball and to result in more serious and severe malfunctioning. Finally the patient sits in his room 24 hours a day, 168 hours a week. His only contact with another human being may be his one hour of therapy a week. When such a condition exists, it may be necessary to interrupt this isolation and to bring the patient into the hospital for a brief period of time in order to help him to establish a level of adaptive capacity in which, once again, he can reach out to others. The hospital can insist that he place himself in juxtaposition to others.

12. Is the patient in need of a redefinition of the sick role? Certain patients who, by their behavior, get themselves placed in other roles, such as the criminal, the sinner, or the "no-good" person, may find it impossible to function in these roles and may need to be redefined in the sick role. Placing an individual in a hospital clearly defines him as a sick person. Such a redefinition, which can sometimes be accomplished by no more than a few hours of hospitalization, may alter the homeostasis so markedly that behavior can become more adaptive.

13. Is the patient in need of therapeutic containment (restraint) for the management of his anxiety? This factor is closely related to item 2 in this list, in which we have mentioned the relief of anxiety that is produced by others' taking over the controls about which the patient has major doubts. In the chronically psychotic patient, one of the major sources

of anxiety may be the recognition of poor impulse control. The patient lives as though he were sitting on top of an active volcano that is about to erupt at any moment. Coming into the hospital may serve the function of having someone else take over the control of the volcano. Simply coming into the hospital markedly lowers the anxiety level in the patient and allows for immediate improvement of functioning. All of us have seen patients who within a matter of hours after coming into the hospital have given up their grossly disorganized behavior to such an extent that one wonders whether hospitalization was indicated. Hospitalization was indicated, but it should be brief. If such a patient had been given tranquilizing medication at the time of admission, the improvement would have been incorrectly attributed to the chemical effect of the medication.

14. Is hospitalization demanded by others, such as the police, a judge, or the family? If the demand for hospitalization is made by others and if hospitalization is not indicated, frequently the question can best be dealt with by a supportive contact with those who are demanding hospitalization. Of course, if these others are the police or a judge, contact may be difficult to carry out and may be contraindicated. On such occasions, it may be necessary to hospitalize a patient against his will and against the will of the therapist. Most states still have systems where the judiciary is in the position of making a final and binding medical decision for which it is not intellectually or emotionally prepared. It is necessary for a therapist to learn to deal with such situations. He must comply and at the same time must make the hospitalization as therapeutic as possible for the patient. For him to identify with the patient and to express to the patient his own anger toward the legal authorities is of no value and may be highly antitherapeutic. The therapist who recognizes that he probably would not have hospitalized this patient at this time can still attempt to make the hospitalization as therapeutic as possible and as brief as possible under the circumstances. If the de-

manding agency is the patient's family and if hospitalization is not indicated, a series of therapeutic contacts with the family members frequently makes it unnecessary to carry out their demands. Often the family simply wants someone to understand their problem. Some recognition of the effort that they have made in caring for the patient will make it possible for them to consider other solutions than "dumping" him. We have already discussed the possible use of hospitalization as a planned vacation for the family.

15. Is hospitalization necessary to remove the patient from a chaotic and pathogenic environment? All too frequently, this reason for hospitalization is not valid, since the therapist tends to judge the patient's environment by his own middle-class standards. We must remember that many chronic patients create their environment to meet their needs for lack of closeness, lack of involvement, and reification of internal chaos in external circumstances. Yet on rare occasions the environment set up by the patient is such that it cannot be adaptively handled by the patient. Even under such circumstances it is best to attempt to find the necessary support and reorganization in the patient's world without removing him from it.

16. Are biological interventions planned that are better carried out in the hospital? When large doses of drugs are to be tried out or initiated and may have possibly serious side effects, treatment may be most safely carried out in the controlled environment of the hospital. Electroconvulsive treatment for emergency control of serious suicidal wishes in depression is always best administered in a hospital setting.

Having outlined the above factors as indications for the use of hospitals in the treatment of chronically ill patients, let us now look at some of the contraindications for hospitalization.

We have already mentioned that the indications for hospitalization and the extent of hospitalization need to be carefully considered. The fact that a good clinician could go into the major psychiatric hospitals of our country and with some effort discharge 60 to 80 per cent of the existing inpatients demonstrates that hospitals are inappropriately used. The observation that with those patients who are discharged, the major problems are those of undoing the effects of chronic alienation and hospitalization demonstrates further that hospitals are generally used antitherapeutically. To some extent misuse of the hospital has resulted from considering hospitalization as the only alternative to not knowing what to do in a difficult clinical situation. It is traditional in American psychiatry that lower-class patients receive hospitalization as the major therapeutic intervention. Since the 1940's and World War II, states have made extensive budgetary expenditures to build new and larger hospitals. Hospital beds throughout the country available to the mentally ill have increased in number. It is well known that this increase has not decreased the occurrence of mental illness, the problems of the mentally ill in the community, or the amount of overcrowding in these hospitals. The one state in the country which did not build new buildings after World War II but rather utilized its available funds for hiring more personnel experienced a decline in the hospital population and a major shift in the direction of treating patients extramurally. In spite of this experience, which occurred some twenty years ago, many therapists still think of the hospital as the major solution to not knowing what to do. Patients are thus frequently caught on the horns of the therapist's dilemma, in which he chooses to do what is safest for himself in terms of avoiding criticism and possible tragedy; but it may not be best for the patient. Decisions for or against hospitalization are difficult and complex, but perhaps our item-by-item outlines exploring the reasons for hospitalization and the contraindications to hospitalization will make possible a more rational and therapeutic use of intramural care.

1. Will hospitalization offer too much gratification of dependency to the patient at this time? This decision, of course,

must be made on the basis of the individual patient's current needs and problems. He may have a great need to be dependent, yet at the same time gratifying his dependency may make it difficult to help him back to a level of functioning such that he can adequately carry on extramurally. The management of the dependency of many chronic patients is a crucial skill required of the clinician. We feel that control of this problem is so essential in treatment of a supportive nature that we have devoted an entire chapter (Chapter 4) to a discussion of it. All of the factors listed in that chapter must be carefully considered in deciding whether at this point in this patient's illness and in his therapeutic transaction with this therapist, hospitalization will have a negative effect on the long-term outcome.

2. Will hospitalization reinforce the patient's failure in life? For many patients, hanging on even marginally in an extramural adjustment represents a victory of will over internal forces. To place a patient in the hospital who has been making it his life's task to function in spite of illness may signal the end of his struggle and may convert him into a patient who no longer struggles. Then his problems with the illness are complicated by prolonged hospitalization, and all of the difficulties of future remotivation and resocialization must be evaluated. Patients to whom hospitalization signals failure rapidly become chronic hospital inmates and show marked "deterioration," which has been erroneously attributed to the disease process rather than to the process of hospitalization. Such patients give up the fight, give up relationships with the outside world, and give up hope for change. This result further alienates them from society, from the family, and from reality. When such a patient is, in the opinion of the therapist, ready for discharge (which may be after only a few days of hospitalization), it takes a major effort to get him back to the level at which he was functioning just before the exacerbation that led to hospitalization. With this kind of patient all possible alternatives to hospitalization

should be explored, even to the extent of creating a hospital-like atmosphere at home by having friends, relatives, or professionals spend 24 hours a day with the patient. In the literature there are descriptions of therapists who see such patients eight hours a day, and some even see them 24 hours a day. Of course, this alternative requires a tremendous amount of interest on the therapist's part and usually considerable funds on the patient's part. Where it can be carried out, however, it is frequently a worth-while substitute for brief hospitalization, especially with patients to whom hospitalization represents failure.

3. Is the removal from contact with reality that occurs when the patient is hospitalized harmful in the management of the patient's chronic problems? That the hospital is different from the outside world is self-evident. That it represents an "unreal" social organization and social structure, with its own spoken and unspoken communications to which the patient must adapt, has frequently been discussed but is not clearly enough understood by therapists deciding for hospitalization. Thus the hospital is seen by some therapists as removing the patient from a complex reality with which he cannot cope to a simple, protected reality with which he does not need to make any effort to cope. We feel that the complexity of the hospital's social reality has not been properly appraised. For some patients, coming into the hospital is a major adaptive task, requiring a capacity for relating to entirely new kinds of authority, peer groups, and spoken and unspoken communications, a task that may be more taxing at that moment than continuing to relate to the already known forces and stresses in the external reality. Furthermore, for the patient to learn to relate to these "unreal" realities in the hospital does not necessarily prepare him for relating more adequately to the realities outside of the hospital. It may, as we have discussed in the preceding section of this chapter, be a useful training device for handling reality, but it should also be recognized that it may train the patient in being

"crazy" in a mental hospital. In some patients who function marginally in the extramural environment, the hold on reality is so tenuous that removal from the need to stay in contact may make it more difficult to re-establish contact. When removal from contact with reality is supported by the therapist in the decision for hospitalization, the patient's retreat into chronic hospitalism may be difficult to counteract.

4. Will the stability of the family in which the patient resided be so affected that a new homeostasis will be established in that group and no longer leave room for the patient? We have mentioned in the preceding section that at times it is useful for a family to take a vacation from a very sick member for a short period of time. Of course, inherent in such a use of hospitalization is the planning for the patient's return at the time of admission to the hospital. If, on the other hand, the patient goes into the hospital and leaves a serious void in the family without any definitive plans having been made for his return, the family may reorganize to such an extent that there is no room for the patient when he wishes to return. Functions may have been taken over by others or by agencies, and the family may have learned that they get along better without him. Then, when the patient is ready to return, his adaptive task is much greater. Not only must he be able to function as well as he had previously, but he must make a new place for himself and find new roles in a new reality. Many patients are unable to do so and thus become chronic hospital patients because there is no place for them in the social structure that previously supported them. This kind of alienation must be considered as a major danger of hospitalization. In part, this problem of discharge can best be prevented at the time of admission, by keeping the family thoroughly involved with the patient and by letting them know that the patient is not being "put away" but is being temporarily and briefly hospitalized in order to help him to return to his previous position in the social structure.

5. What will be the secondary effects of hospitalization

on the patient's life? There are many legal and social consequences of having been hospitalized, especially in a state hospital or a general hospital where this fact becomes a matter of public record. In some states, entrance to a state hospital, especially by commitment, automatically deprives the patient of all citizenship privileges, including the right to carry out his profession, the right to hold a license to drive a car, and sometimes the right to vote. In some states the patient may lose his livelihood as the result of entering a hospital. He may lose his insurability or he may lose his security clearance, and therefore he may no longer be able to carry on his previous job. All of these factors must be carefully considered in terms of local regulations to see whether hospitalization will do more harm than good. What will be the effect on the patient when his employer learns that he has been hospitalized? In some instances, of course, it will have no effect; in other instances, however, the employer may no longer trust him or may not be willing to take him back. Unfortunately, these factors are frequently not considered at the time of a decision for hospitalization. They come to the fore at the time of discharge and may present complicating factors that have nothing to do with the patient's illness, but that may seriously affect the course of his life.

In summary, in any situation in which it is appropriate to consider hospitalizing the patient, the therapist must ask himself the crucial question, "Why now? What biological, social, economic, and other factors have combined to produce the present symptoms of disorganization in this patient at this time?" The theoretical implications of this question, as discussed in Chapter 1, have practical application in considering hospitalization. Obviously, many factors impinge on the patient at the moment when hospitalization is being considered. The psychological, social, familial, medical, economic, and vocational interventions possible in a hospital setting are very different from those that one can effect in outpatient treatment. The doctor's decision, therefore, will turn on his understanding of the relative importance of these factors in the specific patient.

The decision to allow the patient to be discharged from the hospital must, of course, be based on a clear definition of the reasons for hospitalization and a similarly clear outlining of the goals for this specific hospital intervention. As a general principle, we should say that the briefest amount of hospitalization that fulfills these goals is the best hospitalization. This judgment implies that the goals for hospital treatment have been realistic. If one hospitalizes the patient in order to "get him well," the patient is condemned to lifelong invalidism in hospitals. Patients with mental illnesses cannot get well inside a hospital, because getting well implies being able to adapt to and handle reality as it presents itself in the world outside the hospital.

If there is doubt as to when the patient is ready to leave the hospital, the decision should be in favor of letting the patient go. He can always be rehospitalized after his functioning in the outside world has once again been assessed and a need for further hospitalization has been re-established. It is so thoroughly incorporated into our thinking that it has almost become part of our therapeutic prejudice that longer hospitalization is necessarily better hospitalization. As we have mentioned, nothing could be further from the truth. Longer hospitalization is necessarily poorer hospitalization, since it produces all of the secondary effects of chronic and emotional invalidism. The tendency of the hospital is to prolong the intramural state by the difficulties of the mechanics of discharge. Many patients stay in the hospital from several extra days to several extra months so that contacts can be made with the family and certain procedures can be carried out, all of which could just as well be done after the patient has left the hospital. This prolonging of hospitalization can easily be counteracted by having the physician ask himself each morning, "What do I plan to accomplish today with this patient by keeping him in the hospital, and what untoward effects will another day of hospitalization have?" If he cannot give clear answers to these questions to himself each morning, then the patient's hospitalization is not adequately administered and controlled and has the chance of becoming anti-therapeutic rather than therapeutic. If he can answer these questions and discovers that the patient will receive very little benefit from staying another day and that perhaps the same measures could be taken extramurally, it is high time for him to discharge the patient. If he discovers that he has made a mistake and the patient needs further hospitalization, re-hospitalization is easily possible and is preferable to keeping the patient in the hospital too long.

Hospitalization is a potent therapeutic intervention in the management of the chronically ill patient. Like all potent therapeutic tools, it is essential that the physician using it be fully aware of its indications and contraindications, of its side effects and dangers, of its limitations and possibilities. In this chapter we have attempted to outline these indications and contraindications. In the following chapters we shall discuss the details of the processes occurring during hospitalization as a phase of the patient's supportive care.

8

Supportive Care in the Hospital

The kind of treatment planned during hospitalization and the goals of hospitalization depend on the criteria that determined the decision for hospitalization. There are, however, certain unifying principles that can be enunciated. When hospitalization is used for brief periods in the care of the chronically psychotic patient, the unique contribution of the hospital to the total treatment approach is threefold. The hospital can offer a therapeutic environment that focuses consistently on reality, on activity, and on a structured living experience.

The first unifying principle concerns helping the patient in his assessment of reality. It is obviously important that the patient be appraised of the realistic reasons for the decision to hospitalize him, and it is vital that all those concerned with his care in the hospital be realistic about his behavior. The patient must learn to evaluate his own behavior in terms of its appropriateness as judged by others while in the hospital and after he leaves the hospital. In other words, any control, restraint, support, or other intervention between the patient and a member of the hospital staff should be applied with the awareness that the patient must use this experience to formulate his own assessment of his ability to live outside a hospital. It is thus obvious that humoring the patient or conspiring with him not to discuss openly the kind of behavior that made a decision for hospitalization appropriate will inevitably be anti-therapeutic. Realistic discussion of the patient's behavior does not imply, however, that the attitude toward the behavior should be a judgmental one. On the contrary, we must continually strive for the kind of staff-patient interaction in which the patient will come to perceive that we are doing our jobs as therapists when we assess the appropriateness and reality basis of his behavior; but that we, at the same time, accept him as a person and do not demean his worth. It is, of course, obvious that we do make psychiatric and social value judgments about behavior, but we do not make value judgments about the patient as a person. As therapists we make requests of patients regarding their behavior, and we communicate certain expectancies to the patient, yet we do so in such a way that the patient does not have to perceive them as demands with which he must comply in order to gain a feeling of personal worth.

Patients who require supportive care generally suffer much pain and anguish resulting from feelings of utter worthlessness and low self-esteem. The therapist is inevitably seen as an important figure central to the patient's reorganization of himself. In this reorganization the patient differentiates his self-esteem out of his relationship to the therapist. Just as the infant emerges into awareness out of the relationship with the mother, so the disorganized psychotic patient rediscovers and re-establishes his boundaries and adaptive capacities, as well as the appraisal of himself, out of the relationship with his doctor. It is essential that we discuss the patient's behavior with him in such a way that we utilize the therapist-patient relationship to motivate him toward adequately adaptive behavior. We must at the same time avoid tying his sense of worth-whileness to fulfilling demands that come from us.

It is obvious from the foregoing discussion that emphasis on a reality-oriented treatment program does not mean that it should be so impersonally and automatically carried out that there is a lack of gratification from the activities that constitute an important part of the therapeutic regimen. Patients who require supportive care need to be given tasks that they can manage, and they need to be dealt with in staff-patient interactions in such a way that they are allowed to feel gratification and to feel a restoration of their self-esteem. During the period of the patient's hospitalization emphasis should be placed on his actions. His thoughts, feelings, fantasies, dreams, delusions, hallucinations, and other mental phenomena should be de-emphasized. Essentially we must communicate to the patient through our verbal and nonverbal behavior that we hold him accountable for his actions. We let him know that we have compassion and understanding for his feelings and thoughts and that he has as little responsibility and control for them as he does for his heart rate. We help him to understand that thoughts and feelings, like heart rate and heart beat, can lead to uncomfortable awareness and can be altered by emotional states. We help him to recognize that certain prescribed behavior and, at times, medication can alter his uncomfortable feelings and emotional illness, just as in cardiac conduction defects. But we also insist that the goal of treatment is for the patient to take responsibility for his behavior and for the consequences of his behavior. This aspect is crucial to a program of supportive care in a hospital. It is assumed that the decision for hospitalization was not made unless the patient was having difficulty in making his actions appropriate to his situation. Therefore, the time spent in the hospital should have a major influence on his ability to assess his actions as to their appropriateness and their consequences, and no opportunity should be lost in staff-patient interaction to focus on the patient's actions. Because the patient is likely to be concerned about his thoughts and feelings, he will have a tendency to make these a part of his interactions. The hospital staff and the therapist must studiously avoid making their engagements with the patient on these grounds. When such concerns enter the transaction, they should be secondary to a clear emphasis on overt behavior.

As we have stated, all interactions between the doctor (or other representative of the helping situation) and the patient are highly overvalued by the patient. The relationship is never a neutral one, and the task of the helper is to make the situation a therapeutic—rather than an antitherapeutic—one. It follows, therefore, that all of the representatives of the helping situation during a patient's stay in the hospital should agree in their assessment of what will be therapeutic for the patient and should apply with great consistency the measures that will achieve a therapeutic milieu. Such consistency and unanimity of purpose and behavior are not easy to achieve. What follows, therefore, represents our view of what a hospital atmosphere should be: one that is richly endowed with elements designed to enable the patient to adopt successfully the role of patient; that will maximize those of his strengths that will best and soonest enable him to resume his role as a member of the larger community; and that will facilitate the growth of hope in the patient that, whatever the limitations his illness may impose on him, he can function in his life space in a manner sufficiently different from his previous maladaptive pattern that his existence can be maintained with less pain and with more meaning. The therapist who is dealing with a chronically mentally ill person and who has determined that, for any of the reasons outlined in the foregoing chapter, his patient must be removed from the wider community and allowed to restructure his life in the somewhat more limited environment of a hospital should attempt to find for the patient a hospital situation that embodies as many of these elements as possible.

Of overriding importance is the question of what expectancies are communicated to the patient as he enters the hospital. These expectancies are always manifold, and they are both subtle and obvious. By its acceptance of the patient's application for admission the hospital communicates the understanding that—for whatever reason—the patient was no longer able to maintain himself in the situation from which he came. Because the hospital represents a medical setting with the goal of helping sick people, it conveys to the entering patient, "Your acceptance here means that we see your difficulties that brought you here as evidences of illness, and we define you as a sick person whom we will treat." Furthermore, the hospital defines the way in which the person may be a sick patient and communicates that it expects the patient to comport himself accordingly. In some hospitals the expectancy is clearly communicated that irresponsible, destructive, or violent behavior is foreseen and expected. In such places the incoming patient sees no rooms but locked ones, he is allowed nothing sharp or pointed, he is not allowed matches, and his belt and shoelaces are taken from him. As the patient acquaints himself with his environment he sees many reminders that he is expected to be the kind of sick patient who is crazy, harmful, and dangerous. His own fears of his destructive feelings are thus compounded, and the probability is increased that, in his confused, disorganized, or otherwise impaired adaptive state, the patient will comply with this expectancy.

The story is told of a rural state hospital in which the great majority of the attendants maintained the belief that violent behavior among the patients increased markedly when the moon was full. When a new superintendent disparaged this belief as a superstition, they brought out records of orders for restraint and seclusion that were highly correlated with the moon's phase. The superintendent was able to find a few attendants who agreed with him that the belief was a super-stition, and he staffed a small section of the hospital with these attendants. In this section of the hospital, of course, the degree to which patients required restraint and seclusion became totally unrelated to lunar phenomena, whereas the old cor-related pattern persisted in the rest of the hospital. The story does not, however, have a happy ending: when the superin-tendent confronted the entire staff with the results from the experiment, the attendants persisted in their superstition, and the superintendent became discouraged and moved on to an-other professional affiliation.

It is clear that our expectancies are important in eliciting behavior from the patient, and, fortunately, there are increas-ingly large numbers of hospitals where the expectancy of violent and destructive behavior is not present among the staff (or implicit in the hospital architecture or administration) and is thus not communicated to the patient. A growing num-ber of hospitals no longer practice the depersonalizing and dehumanizing admission procedures that were traditional for so long in psychiatric institutions. A routine in which a con-fused and frightened person is brought manacled by the police, is divested of his clothing and valuables (such as wed-ding ring, wallet, identification card, and pictures of loved ones), is roughly scrubbed under a shower, is tagged with a number, and is dressed in ill-fitting and unsightly hospital clothing would seem to have been designed with the intent of removing a person's identity, as well as his dignity. Certainly it does not convey to him the expectancy that he will be a responsible person who will utilize those functions that remain relatively unimpaired by illness to respond to the helping institution's efforts to return him as soon as possible to the society from which he came.

As the person who requires hospitalization is admitted, he should immediately be made a part of an organized, active program in which the staff is oriented toward helping him to mobilize all available family and community resources, as well as his own inner resources. He should be, in the first instance, introduced by name to the treatment personnel and to his fellow patients. He should be made aware that his family is being involved in his treatment and that he should expect to interact with them in a way commensurate with his therapeutic needs. The family and the patient will thus perceive that, although the patient has become a member of a special therapeutic community, he remains a participant in a familial and social community.

If the patient is markedly confused or unrealistic, the therapeutic program will at first relieve him of responsibility for decision-making. The expectation will be communicated to him that he will participate in the activities of the therapeutic community, and he will be reminded in a very specific and detailed way (even led to it, if necessary) of each response that is expected of him. He will receive continuous "feedback" from his environment about the adequacy of his reality-testing, and, as his degree of illness subsides, he will be encouraged to take an increasing amount of responsibility for fitting himself into the structure of the therapeutic regimen in a relatively autonomous manner.

If at first he reacts, because of his confusion and fright, with belligerence, it should quickly be demonstrated to him that he will not be permitted to lose self-control. A hospital staff that is well trained in the care of mentally ill patients knows that an effective deterrent to uncontrolled behavior is the "show of force," in which the patient is confronted by three or four of the staff who talk with him about his feelings of impending loss of control and reassure him that he will be protected against behavior that he can only regret later when he is less confused and frightened. Sometimes it is appropriate, when the patient is afraid of his fellow patients, to seclude him from them, but this result can usually be accomplished by having several staff members accompany him to his room and having a professional person stay near him. The patient should not be allowed to remain secluded from human contact when he is dealing with such overwhelming feelings, because his reality-testing is so impaired that he needs continually to be reminded of the structure of the therapeutic situation and of the necessity of becoming a better functioning member of the therapeutic community.

Regarding belligerent or "violent" behavior by the mentally ill, it can be stated categorically that if a member of a hospital staff is struck by a patient, he has erred in the performance of his therapeutic task. He has not adequately assessed the turmoil within the patient, he has assumed too much individual responsibility in helping the patient maintain self-control, or he has done something actively antitherapeutic in his interaction with the patient.

Special mention must be made of the treatment approach to the chronically ill patient who presents withdrawal as a major symptom. It is essential, of course, correctly to differentiate this symptom from depression. Withdrawal, which is only one variable of disturbed behavior, responds well to the three previously outlined basic principles of hospital care—reality, activity, and structure. With a withdrawn patient, a special effort must be made to offer constantly and consistently the opportunity of human interaction. Treating a withdrawn patient is somewhat like feeding a bird from an extended hand. The relationship is offered, the hand is held out, the fear of entrapment is minimized, and the rewards of interaction are as clearly presented as possible. When the withdrawn patient begins to respond to this offer of a relationship, care must be taken not to frighten him away. Any demand for more closeness than the patient can tolerate can result in further withdrawal and in greater difficulty in guiding the patient out of the prison in which he has incarcerated himself.

The patient whose major symptom at the time of admission to the hospital is depression may require the introduction of a special transactional technique that limits and monitors the amount of gratification he receives. Most depressed patients respond poorly to sympathy and gratification. In fact, in many patients the depression deepens when they are given praise, gratification, and sympathy. (A notable exception to this effect is the rare adult patient with an anaclitic depression, who requires much gratification.)

The depressed, chronically psychotic patient needs to be treated in a structured, realistic, and activity-oriented environment. In addition, however, his assigned activities and staff interactions should be carried out with a matter-of-fact attitude. The interpersonal transactions must be used to convey to the patient that the therapeutic team understands how he feels, but that just the same he is expected to carry out his assigned activities. When he responds with "I can't," we counter with, "I know you feel as though you can't, but this assignment (meeting, group therapy, ward activity) is part of your treatment, and we insist that you do it." If the patient cannot then respond, we may go even further, to the extent of assisting him physically with the task. Every task should be assigned keeping in mind the amount of gratification provided by the activity itself. For example, in occupational therapy the completion of projects that will win praise from the therapist or other patients is obviously a gratifying activity. On the other hand, preparing material for others to use in the completion of projects is much less gratifying. Similarly, work activities that consist of cleaning windows or walls that remain clean for some time and that may win praise from the nursing staff or from other patients are also gratifying. In contrast, the cleaning of bathrooms or floors that are immediately used again offers very little gratification to the patient. In a well-run hospital, all of the activities and staff-patient interactions can be controlled so that the amount of gratification offered the patient will be consistent with his therapeutic needs, as judged by the therapist. It becomes obvious, then, that the hospital milieu can only operate consistently if the treatment team is well led and if every member of the team is fully aware of the attitudes and activities prescribed for each patient. The value of a hospital experience for the patient is seriously limited when the various members of the treatment team do not agree in their approach to him.

It is our view that brevity should be a cardinal principle of psychiatric hospitalization. If the hospital's program is formulated in terms of brief interventions, this approach will be both implicitly and explicitly communicated to the patient upon his admission and throughout his stay, and he will respond by preserving and fostering those of his strengths that will be important in adjusting in his community. The converse situation, in which the patient is confronted on every hand with the expectation that his illness will require protracted hospitalization, will erode his healthy adaptive functions and will bring about an atrophy of disuse of his capacity for autonomous functioning.

One can see, when one visits a psychiatric hospital whose function is largely custodial, that there are both obvious and subtle communications of an attitude that the patient is not a responsible person. It is fairly obvious, for example, when a patient describes himself as an "inmate" of the institution, that he is responding to a structure that has emphasized incarceration as one of its functions. When one is served in the hospital cafeteria by a waitress who states with pride that she has worked there for five years but that she "may" be released next year, it is readily apparent that she has had to make a serious readjustment of her appraisal of herself as a woman with a responsible place in a family and a community. When one sees large numbers of patients with poor dentition, and inquiry reveals that the hospital's budget allows for dental extractions but not for fillings or prophylaxis, one can deduce that budgetary considerations have been given precedence over the human dignity and self-esteem of the patients. When one hears hospital personnel addressing all patients by their first names, one realizes they are addressing themselves to the irresponsible, infantile aspects of these patients, rather than to their adult, responsible selves.

These and many other examples reveal the dangers of long-term hospitalization. Legislators, hospital personnel, and the general public are all prone to think in terms of the public economy rather than in terms of the economics of human needs when they must deal with planning for long-term hospitalization for the mentally ill. The psychiatric hospital that can be conceptualized as providing a useful, brief service in intervening in chronic mental illness can structure itself along very different lines. The public must be made aware of the fact that repeated brief hospitalizations in the life of a chronically mentally ill person may make possible a more nearly optimal functioning in that person than a long stay in a hospital. It seems obvious that the expectancies to which the person must respond in a long hospitalization bring about behaviors that are inimical to his good adjustment in the larger community.

The therapist who is treating a mentally ill person may decide, when hospitalization is appropriate, to admit the patient to a local community general hospital. When the patient and his family need a short time in which to regroup their forces for dealing with the effects of the patient's illness, or when the doctor needs a short period of time in which to explore other resources for the patient, this form of hospitalization can be a most useful way in which the doctor may intervene in the illness process. Such a hospitalization has the advantage of implying that its duration will be relatively brief. There are other expectancies that may be equally important and that may be somewhat antitherapeutic. If the staff of the general hospital conveys the attitude common to many uninformed people that a psychiatric patient is dangerous, it will add greatly to the patient's discomfort. Also, of course, there is little in the way of an activity program for the patient to become involved in, and he is likely to be put to bed—a decision that may be disorganizing for the patient. As long as the hospitalization can be brief and the practitioner feels that he can exercise appropriate control of the hospital milieu, hospitalization in a community general hospital may be one of the richer untapped resources of the helping situation.

A problem shared by both the general hospital and the psychiatric hospital is a tendency to reward sick behavior and to ignore relatively healthy behavior. A patient who is behaving in an inappropriate manner elicits considerable attention from the nursing and other staff, whereas a patient who goes about his affairs behaving as if he were normal excites no attention, nor does he elicit special consideration from the personnel. It is important that the therapist and all of the personnel of the hospital situation interact with the patient and reflect openly their assessment of his behavior, whether that behavior be bizarre or appropriate, sick or well.

It is apparent from the foregoing statements that not only must the hospital be staffed with professionally skilled personnel, it must also have a rich ratio of staff to patients in order to accomplish its tasks. Lest it be thought that the hospital's primary task is to control patients' behavior, we hasten to add that, on the contrary, having a sufficient number of trained personnel insures against destructive behavior and makes available a staff that can structure a therapeutic program rich in activities of a realistic nature for patients in the therapeutic milieu. In other words, we are not advocating staffing a hospital with burly attendants who see their role as waiting to quell disturbances; the staff should be selected because they represent a variety of skills in interpersonal interactions, and, when disturbances arise, they can communally demonstrate the external controls that the patient requires.

A therapeutic milieu can be created by psychiatrists, psychiatric nurses and attendants, social workers, psychologists, occupational therapists, recreational therapists, housekeeping personnel, and many others. Whatever the discipline represented by the staff member, he should see his task as working with his fellow staff members to structure a therapeutic environment that is richly supplied with realistic activities and abundant opportunities for meaningful, realistic interpersonal interactions. The media for such therapeutic experiences for the patient can be occupational therapy, group therapy, psychodrama, recreation, individual psychotherapy, family therapy, and many more. Although there will obviously be certain of the professional staff who specialize in one of these media, we are of the opinion that the most creatively realized hospital programs are those in which disciplinary lines are crossed freely, and where members of the hospital staff collaborate in imaginative ways to work out a variety of therapeutic activities for patients.

The foregoing discussion has outlined those techniques of supportive care that are especially suitable for the phase of treatment that must be carried out in the hospital. Yet we must emphasize once again that in the hospital, as well as out of the hospital, the major vehicle for treatment is the human interaction. In hospital settings where much personnel is available and therefore much interaction is possible, excellent care for the patient is possible. We have described in this chapter the considerations that must guide the staff in interacting with patients, but we must also emphasize that the patient should have as many interactions with the staff as possible. Patients who require hospitalization come because they find it difficult to function with their distress in society. They seek from the hospital relief from their distress. We must provide this relief through human interaction. The more ably the patient can use fellow human beings for comfort and relief, the more quickly he will respond to the hospital intervention. The less ably he can use human interaction, the more difficult it is to treat him. Thus, the combination of the treatment program and the human interaction provides the essentials of what the hospital has to offer the patient in helping him to function once again extramurally. When the patient is ready to leave the hospital, appropriate preparations should be made for him to resume supportive care outside. While the patient is still in the hospital, preparations should be made for his aftercare. He should know when his first treatment appointment will be after leaving the hospital; he should know whom he will see and in what location he will be seen; and the details of his activity between the termination of hospital treatment and the first aftercare appointment should be meticulously explored. If the reasons for the hospitalization are thoroughly understood by the patient, if the treatment in the hospital has been brief and well handled, with the patient taking increasing responsibility for his actions each day as he progresses toward leaving the hospital, and if the transition to aftercare is thoroughly understood by the patient, the difficulties of leaving the hospital can be minimized. Where the preparations have not been made, or where the hospitalization has been prolonged, resulting in the secondary problems of chronic hospitalism, leaving the hospital will be difficult and frightening, and the patient may require lengthy rehabilitation, remotivation, and resocialization.

If the hospital experience has been a therapeutic one for the patient, the hospital can become a symbol of the helping situation that can be called upon at a later date as an important link in the chain of supportive care. For some patients the mere knowledge that the hospital is there, is available, and has been part of the treatment reality will be sufficient to offer much in helping him through future crises of disorganization and hopelessness. On many occasions hospitalization is not necessary so long as the patient is reassured by the knowledge that hospital care is available to him if a future disorganization makes it necessary to consider this aspect of supportive care.

9

Outpatient Treatment

How does the chronically mentally ill person become an outpatient? There are many avenues through which a person comes to be identified as suffering from such an illness and as needing supportive care.

One has only to travel through a "skid row" or a "Hyde Park" area of a large city to realize that many persons who frequent these areas represent the chronically mentally ill who have gone unrecognized and untreated. They cling marginally to the fringes of the communities of which they are a part, but they have slowly lost what interpersonal skills and responsible social functioning once were theirs, and they are now not only untreated but perhaps untreatable. For it is the task of supportive care to halt the erosion of adequate functioning, to help the person to maintain himself as a responsible social unit within the limitations imposed by his illness. We do not ascribe to supportive treatment the ability to "save lost souls," nor do we consider redemptory zeal useful in our work. We do not need to seek out patients who can benefit from supportive care; they are to be found everywhere. Indeed, because of their need to have others concerned about them, they will seek out help whenever a helping agent can be identified.

Formerly, it was one of the recognized tasks of the family unit to provide "support and care" for one of its number whose behavior gave evidence that he could not function at the social level that propriety required. As societies grew more complex in their organization, and as responsibility of men toward their fellows became more diffuse and more impersonally organized, various publicly supported agencies came to assume increasing responsibility for those poorly functioning members of society who were not excluded from it by being regarded as criminal or insane. Thus it is that in today's society one of the most frequent providers of supportive care is the welfare agency. Unfortunately, many of these agencies are sparsely staffed, offering little in the way of professional consultation, and the large group of chronically mentally ill who are to be found on the agencies' rolls receive only the welfare funds of the community and not the interpersonal supportive relationship that such agencies could provide. Where adequate staffing and consultation are available, on the other hand, excellent supportive care is being provided to many thousands of the chronically mentally ill by persons who are not formally identified as psychotherapists.

Such agencies frequently refer their clients to a practicing psychiatrist for evaluation. When the latter determines the patient's need for supportive care and when the agency can be mobilized to continue such care, the psychiatrist can exercise a useful function by encouraging the patient to continue his contacts with the helping agency.

There are many other avenues through which the chronically ill come to the psychiatrist's office for evaluation. A frequent source of referrals is the nonpsychiatrist specialist or the general practitioner. In our contacts with these physicians we are accustomed to hear estimates that from one half to three fourths of their practices consist of patients whose condition is both chronic and not significantly organic in nature. As we all know, such patients are sometimes trying because they seem refractory to treatment, yet the psychiatrist can be of service both to the patient and to his medical colleague when he identifies the need of the patient for a supportive and continuing relationship with his doctor. We shall discuss later the techniques for making such consultations, but we may detail here some examples of the kind of medical problem seen in such consultations.

School health physicians frequently encounter students whose difficulties, both scholastic and interpersonal, reveal the presence of a chronic schizophrenic process. This process sometimes goes unrecognized until a referral is made to a psychiatrist. Disturbed behavior is distressing to the families and peers of the person so disturbed, and it frequently calls him to the attention of the physician. Indeed, it is precisely because of the concern engendered in friends and family that it becomes appropriate to mobilize this concern and to utilize the "medical presence," to manage the maladaptive, alienating behavior, so that further alienation and social disarticulation are avoided. For example, a student who, on moving from elementary to high school, shows a marked change in academic performance will first be identified as a school problem. A parent-teacher conference reveals that he has shown marked changes in behavior at home, including daydreaming and withdrawal, and that frequent treatment by the family physician for multiple somatic complaints has not been of help. A detailed evaluation by the consulting psychiatrist reveals that the general decline of function in all spheres represents the onset of a chronic impairment of an adaptation now overtaxed by the more complex social, sexual, and intellectual environment of the high school.

The obstetrician is another frequent source of psychiatric referrals, when he is dealing with a post-partum psychosis.

Rather than constituting a disease entity in itself, this reaction is nearly always a reflection of a tenuously adjusted personality confronted by a major life stress. For a woman with limited adaptive capacities, motherhood requires a shift in role identification that sometimes overtaxes her, coming, as it does, at a time when she is also required to make a new physiological adaptation. Another not uncommon referral from the obstetrician is the husband of the post-partum patient, whose disturbed behavior represents a psychotic reaction precipitated by the role demands of fatherhood. Similarly, the gynecologist often deals with the chronically psychotic patient who comes to him when she is reacting to the stress of the menopause by a disorganization of her adaptation.

From the surgeon's office one encounters the patient with a long history of surgical interventions, none of which has succeeded in eradicating the source of the pain of which the patient complains. The orthopedic surgeon frequently refers for psychiatric evaluation the patient whose complaint of low back pain has remained refractory to all forms of treatment, and who is now being considered for a laminectomy or fusion. The plastic surgeon often wisely chooses to refer to the psychiatrist for evaluation the patient who has come to the conclusion that all of his life's difficulties will be solved if his appearance can be altered.

Similar referrals come from the offices of many non-psychiatrist physicians when a patient has come to be known as a hypochondriac, whose symptoms are ephemeral but incapacitating, and whose pains have shifting loci. Another familiar problem in psychiatric referrals is the obese patient, whose previously good adjustment has been shattered when there has been a marked reduction in weight. In the patient who overeats as a way of coping, the interruption of this behavior with diets and with medications such as amphetamines may occasion a disorganization of functioning of psychotic proportions.

Because the doctor is placed by the public in a helping

role, he is frequently the person to whom people turn when their essential need is for supportive care. Many other persons, however, become identified as potential helpers or as agencies through which help can be provided for persons who do not recognize their need for it. The pastor who ministers to his congregation, the judge who must assess the behavior of individual human beings in the light of standards of behavior that societies have codified in the form of laws, the prison official who comes to recognize that his prisoners' behavior seems to represent something more than willful socially destructive behavior, and the officer in the armed forces whose responsibility for the behavior of his men runs around the clock—all of these persons may be seen as helpers or as avenues through which help may be obtained. All of them are likely to be in a position to make referrals to a consulting psychiatrist for the determination of an individual's amenability to supportive care, and all of them can provide it under proper guidance. Some persons come to psychiatric outpatient care not because of their own anxiety or discomfort, but because their families can no longer tolerate their disruptive behavior.

We should mention, finally, the situation in which the patient refers himself to the psychiatrist's office. This circumstance may be quite different from the referrals mentioned in the foregoing paragraphs, for one can properly infer in this situation that the person has already identified himself as requiring some intervention in the area of "mental" or "emotional" diagnosis or treatment. When the patient has correctly identified the psychiatric nature of his illness, the doctor and the patient begin their transaction with considerable advantages over those situations in which such an identification must be worked through. Nevertheless, it is not infrequent that the psychiatrist hears the patient complaining of physical symptoms, and he should then ask of himself and of the patient why he has come with such a complaint to someone who specializes in the diagnosis and treatment of other than physical complaints. Almost invariably the answer is that the patient has identified the problem as belonging in the psychiatrist's area of specialization, but that he needs to deal metaphorically with the nature of his malfunctioning. Not only is the stigmatizing nature of society's attitudes toward mental illness of causal significance in such a maneuver; the patient himself has an understandable reluctance to admit that he is unable to manage his affairs autonomously.

Identifying the person in the sick role is one of the most sensitive and vital points of the doctor-patient transaction in supportive care, and it is a *sine qua non* of successful supportive care. If a psychiatrist is to conduct the treatment, the illness must be identified as psychiatric. If the psychiatrist is seeing the patient in consultation for another doctor, he must make the identification as to the presence or absence of a mental illness for the referring doctor, but it is possible for the nonpsychiatrist to conduct a patient's supportive care without the patient's having identified himself as mentally ill. The important variable here is the identification of illness and the patient's acceptance of the sick role. Unlike some theorists who currently advise against the management of personal difficulties in a medical setting, we believe that this function is correctly placed in the historical tradition of medicine. It constitutes not only a self-esteem-saving measure but even at times a life-saving one. With a patient who has been led to think of himself as bad or evil and who therefore ruminates about suicide, the physician can introduce a new perspective when he helps the patient to realize that he has an illness that is treatable and manageable.

When the careful clinician detects an emotionally disharmonious life style and disturbances in the stream of thought behind the personal difficulties caused by the awkward, stilted, or bizarre relationships that the patient demonstrates in a familial, social, or vocational context, he is probably dealing with a person who will benefit from being defined as a patient. It can make a decisive difference and provide great therapeutic leverage to help the person to redefine himself in the patient role instead of in the role of criminal or sinner.

Whether or not the source that referred the person to the psychiatrist's office can also serve as the source of a continuing relationship once the consultation is completed makes a great deal of difference. Not only must the psychiatrist evaluate the patient, he must also investigate the availability to the patient of other supportive relationships. In making his evaluation the psychiatrist must remember that the patient may interpret his referral to the psychiatrist as having constituted a rejection by a possible supportive relationship, and the consultant must bear in mind the possibility that re-referring the patient to the original source will be interpreted as still another rejection. The consultant should therefore take care to explore with the patient the meaning of the referral; he should determine the patient's feelings about the referring source and should avail himself of as much collateral information as he can bring to bear on the question of the patient's ability to function.

If he makes the decision to return the patient to the referring source or to another source of supportive care, he must be sure that he has allowed the patient to arrive at a feeling that this referral does not constitute a further rejection. He must make adequate communication of his findings to the person who will provide the supportive care. It has been our experience that the psychiatrist who acts as consultant frequently does not perceive that the person who referred the patient to him for consultation is capable of providing supportive care, but that in order to do so he needs the psychiatrist's support and "approval." If the consulting psychiatrist does an adequate job of outlining the kinds of interactions that seem to him appropriate for the patient, and if the referring source is helped to see how the relationship can continue to be supportive to the patient, he is providing a valuable function for the patient and for the community.

In the situation in which the psychiatrist is to be the

continuing supportive person in the medical transaction with
the patient, it is essential, as we have mentioned, that he assist
the patient in identifying himself in the sick role. We find that
frequently it is useful for the doctor to convey to the patient
that his difficulties constitute a mental illness. Patients react
with a variety of responses to such a confrontation. Some
patients will continue to emphasize somatic complaints. The
psychiatrist must then respond by attending to these complaints (or by referring the patient to another physician for
their care) but, at the same time, he must deal openly with
the patient about the mental nature of the illness. He must
help the patient to see that learning techniques of recognizing
and managing these mental manifestations is primary to the
patient's adequate functioning and comfort. Another typical
response to a frank statement by the psychiatrist of the mental
nature of the illness appears when the patient expresses great
relief that the confusing and disturbing occurrences in his
life can be understood and labeled as mental illness. To see
that a doctor can look at his reaction patterns as symptomatic
of illness, and that there is in the relationship an implicit
desire on the part of the doctor to help, can be a very hopeful
step for a person who has felt himself increasingly alienated
from his fellow men. Not uncommonly the patient who is trying to adopt the sick role translates this new-found attitude
of hopefulness into an expectation of cure, and it becomes
important for the psychiatrist to convey a different sort of
expectancy to the patient. He should help the patient to see
that the first priority of therapeutic effort must aim at the
management of the symptoms that disturb the patient's adequate functioning and that the process of "improving" or
"getting better" will be a slow one—that the therapeutic
relationship should be looked at as a long-term one. We think
that it is best to avoid the term "cure"; in the first place we
do not believe that it is correct to talk about cures in the illnesses with which we are dealing, and, in the second place,
we need to utilize every opportunity to convey to the patient,

both implicitly and explicitly, that he need not expect that the relationship will have a termination point in the finite future. This point bears much repetition in supportive care, and the patient will provide many occasions on which the therapist can remind him that his primary task is the management of the realities of his daily living and that this purpose does not involve a formulation of what kind of person the patient will be when the therapy is "finished."

The psychiatrist should, as soon as he has made the determination that the patient is suffering from a chronic mental illness and that he intends to undertake the patient's treatment, establish a frequency of contact with the patient that he feels the patient can tolerate and that the psychiatrist is prepared to continue indefinitely. It is seldom appropriate to make this contact more frequent than once a week; often once every other week or once a month will be optimal for chronically mentally ill patients. The primary reason for not establishing an initially greater frequency lies in our observation that the group of patients about whom we are speaking usually misinterprets a reduction or an increase in the frequency of visits and reacts poorly to an alteration. They may see a reduction in the frequency of visits as a rejection, as a sign that they are getting better, as a sign that they are getting worse, or as a sign that the therapist fears and cannot tolerate their behavior, when none of these factors may have been involved in the change. Similarly, an increase in frequency may be misinterpreted as signaling greater demands, as an attempt to establish a degree of closeness that the patient cannot tolerate, or as an assault on the patient's defense pattern. Whatever a patient's reaction to a change may be, his behavior may deviate in the direction of increasingly severe symptoms, because in this way he communicates to the therapist that he feels that he has been misunderstood. Likewise, with respect to the length of the "hour" the therapist should establish the length of visit that he feels the patient can best tolerate and that he is prepared to commit out of his office schedule over a long period of time. This decision will mean that the therapist will rather quickly establish with a chronically ill patient a routine of supportive care that involves the patient's coming for perhaps a half-hour visit once every two weeks or once every month. In this way the psychotherapist whose primary interest is in insight (expressive) treatment can still be an effective agent in the lives of a great many patients and at the same time can meet his responsibility toward dealing with a major public health problem. He can expand the effectiveness of his treatment energies by allotting a portion of his office day to these brief, infrequent, supportive-care visits. He can act as a consultant and evaluate patients referred for possible supportive care while continuing in his more traditional role.

The actual techniques of supportive care in an outpatient setting are essentially no different from those described in other chapters of this book. The emphasis is always on reality assessment, and on action rather than on thought and feeling. The atmosphere is nonjudgmental and nondemanding. The goals of the outpatient treatment of the chronically mentally ill are essentially (1) to help the patient to manage his life in such a way as to minimize the dysfunction and disruption caused by the illness; (2) to help the patient to learn to be sensitive to his behavior; (3) to remind him of the symptoms that were present during past exacerbations of his illness; and (4) to assist in working out the degree of delicate balance that it is necessary for him to maintain if he is to live as if he were not chronically mentally ill. It is useful and necessary to have periodic "review" sessions in which the patient is reminded of his past dysfunction. These reviews should occur at times when his functioning is relatively good, so that together the doctor and the patient can summarize recent periods of good adjustment. This contrast can serve as reinforcement for the further maintenance of good adjustment and can and should be carried out in such a way as not to imply that the therapy is moving toward termination or toward a diminution of concern and interest.

Supportive care in an outpatient setting, then, can be

viewed as embodying the same principles as outlined in other sections of this book. It is distinct in that it does not occur as a consequence of hospitalization, and it is not necessarily translated into the psychiatric context. Even though providing such care requires that the therapist accept limited goals and exercise heroic patience, the returns to the patient for a minimal investment of the therapist's time are great, and a logistically significant avenue is thus opened to the solution of a major public health problem.

10

Management of the Therapy "Hour"

The management of the therapeutic encounter involves the translation of the theoretical formulations given in previous portions of this book into practical tactics. The treatment contact, or treatment "hour," must reinforce the therapeutic intent of the doctor-patient relationship. It must help the patient to maintain a feeling of the openness of the future; and it must help him to reinforce a separation of internal from external reality. (We use the term "therapy 'hour'" to indicate that—however much we may depart from a traditionalist conception of the therapist as a "blank screen"—we consider such a doctor-patient encounter to be therapeutic in effect, as well as in intent; and we surround the word *hour* with quotation marks to indicate that this traditional term has little temporal significance in this context and that, whether one talks about a fifteen-minute encounter or a longer one, it should be tailored to the need and tolerance of the patient in supportive care.) The encounter must support the attitude in the patient that he is responsible for what he does, not for what he thinks, wishes, or fantasies.

The chronic patient who is supported in his functioning through regular therapeutic contacts has great expectations of the therapist. The patient makes demands on the therapist that are commensurate with his needs. In an atmosphere where the patient expects omniscience from the therapist, each event of the contact is overvalued and overinterpreted. Each word, each gesture, each detail of the transaction is inspected by the patient for evidence of acceptance or rejection, for evidence of the therapist's attitude toward the patient's ideas and conduct, and for hints of demands and suggestions by the therapist. Even those aspects of the therapeutic encounter for which the therapist has no direct responsibility—such as the mood of the receptionist, the parking facilities, the telephone operator's approach, and the format of the appointment slip—enter into the therapeutic transaction. Since the patient holds the therapist responsible for all aspects of the therapeutic encounter, nothing that occurs within the context of that encounter can be viewed as neutral. Each act or omission of an act by the therapist is necessarily either therapeutic or antitherapeutic, that is to say, it will either further the purpose of the transaction or interfere with it. It will either support the patient in his functioning or it will undermine the supportive intent of the transaction. When we observe the small details of the therapeutic transaction, it becomes apparent that many of them can be antitherapeutic rather than therapeutic, if left to chance alone.

Even before the therapy hour begins, the problem arises as to the scheduling and frequency of appointments. How frequently the patient should be seen depends to some extent on his needs. Some patients require a contact on a weekly basis, whereas others can be effectively supported with one fifteen-minute encounter once a month. In scheduling the frequency of therapeutic encounters we must remind ourselves that, although each encounter is a prop for the support of the patient's functioning, it can also be a stress for the patient. This stress arises out of the patient's need to relate to the therapist, to read the therapist's wishes and demands, and to try to comply with them. For many patients the therapeutic encounter is seen as requiring a closeness in an interpersonal situation that exceeds their capacity to respond. Therefore, a therapeutic encounter that is more frequent than once or twice a week can sometimes be more stressful than no treatment at all. A change in the frequency of appointments is usually a major disturbance in supportive contacts with patients. If the therapist increases the frequency of appointments in response to his anxiety about the patient's illness or malfunctioning, this anxiety is quickly transmitted to the patient and becomes antitherapeutic. Although it would seem appropriate to increase the frequency of supportive visits when the patient is not functioning well, as a method of expressing concern and interest, actually such a change may have the opposite effect. It may bring on further exacerbation of symptoms and disorganization of functioning. Similarly, a decrease in the frequency of sessions may be contraindicated. Although the therapist may see decreasing the frequency of appointments as evidence of his recognition of a patient's increased functioning and strength, the patient may see it as rejection. Whereas in expressive psychotherapy the problem of termination can be worked through, decreasing the number of appointments in supportive care is a much more complex problem. In assessing the possibility of decreasing the frequency of contacts, one may not always rely on the patient's verbalization. At times the patient may, indeed, request a decrease in the number of appointments. To comply with such a request automatically may have disastrous results. Even though he may say, "I'm feeling so much better; perhaps I only need to see you once a month. I can really use the money better for other things," his latent communication may be, "I think you're probably tired of me. I think very soon you will reject me. Therefore, I'm offering to leave you before you can leave me and hurt me." Within the context of the latent communication it becomes evident that the therapist must have his third ear constantly "tuned in" so that he can respond to the metaphor rather than to the overt verbal communication. Over the course of long-term supportive care, the therapist must also recognize the possibility that an increase in the frequency or length of contact during exacerbations of psychotic symptoms and a decrease in contact during periods of improved functioning can serve as a reward for illness and a lack of reward for healthy behavior. In such circumstances one often sees patients "unaccountably" becoming sicker.

Since each detail of the therapeutic contact is overvalued by the patient, attention must be paid to every detail in designing treatment. If, for example, the interview is scheduled on a regular basis once a week, appointments must be kept carefully and guarded for the patient. Even though it may make no real difference to the therapist whether the patient is slightly late or whether he calls to change an appointment, considerable care must be taken to interpret the patient's requests by listening to the latent language. The patient who says, "Would it be all right for me not to come next Thursday because that's the day I want to take my laundry to the cleaners?" may in fact be asking (in latent language) "Do you really think this therapy is important for me, and is it as important to you as it is to me?" If the therapist were to respond by saying, "Yes, go ahead and take your laundry to the cleaners and come in whenever you have some time," he would be communicating within the metaphor to the patient, "I don't think your treatment is very important to you, and I'm certainly quite bored with you and welcome a vacation from this encounter. You might as well do your laundry as come here." The patient whom we are describing in this volume—the patient who is in need of supportive care—is highly sensitive to rejection. Generally, the chronic schizophrenic patient responds to inferred rejection by withdrawal and malfunctioning. It would be better to manage scheduling of the next appointment by stating, "I think your therapy hour is very important, and if at all possible you must try to keep it. Isn't there some way you can arrange to take your laundry at some other time, so that it does not interfere with this therapy hour? Your therapy is very important in helping you." Such a response would be reassuring to the patient. Such a response would communicate, "I think what we're doing here is important. I want you to be here. I will be here to help you."

As part of the structure of the therapeutic encounter, attention should be given to starting and ending on time. Punctual starting can signify the importance that the therapist gives to the therapeutic encounter. Many patients test how interested and how concerned the therapist is by coming late. If the therapist overlooks tardiness, the omission may reinforce the patient's low self-esteem. A slight oversight like not mentioning tardiness convinces some patients that the therapist would really rather not see them. Patients test for concern in many other ways, such as missed appointments, mistaken appointments, arriving early, or transportation difficulties. All of these are examples of the metaphors with which patients test the therapist's concern and interest.

Disguised communication through latent language occurs constantly throughout the transaction. Constant vigilance and alertness by the therapist make it possible to manage the therapeutic transaction in such a way as to lead to reintegration and improved functioning. The clues to the meaning of the latent communication must come from the patient, but a basic understanding that everything the patient says or does during the therapeutic encounter is overvalued, personally significant, and related to security operations in the relationship with the therapist makes it possible to decode the metaphor of communication. As a general rule in the treatment of the chronic schizophrenic patient, it is best to respond within the metaphor that the patient chooses.

This technique demonstrates one of the differences between expressive psychotherapy and supportive care. When the therapist recognizes and understands the metaphor of the neurotic patient, he will lift this content out of the metaphor to confront the patient with what he is really saying. In the treatment of the chronic psychotic patient, on the other hand, it is more supportive to continue relating within the metaphor that the patient chooses, while waiting for him to lift the communication out of the metaphor. The remoteness of the metaphor from the "real" communication gives the therapist important clues as to the amount of anxiety the patient feels in the area of the communication. If, for example, the patient says, "When I was a young boy, we had a neighbor who frequently talked about a friend he had when he was a child and lived in Europe, and this friend beat his wife on a regular basis," the patient is more anxious about his own aggressive impulses than if he had said, "Yesterday my brother told me that occasionally he feels like beating his wife." The therapist who is tuned in on this patient's latent language and who can respond appropriately within the metaphor is frequently rewarded by the patient's lifting the communication into a direct statement. As the patient begins to feel that he is understood, as he becomes more comfortable with the content of his thoughts, he will be able to drop the disguise and the remoteness of the metaphor. A patient who spent many appointments discussing his mechanical difficulties with his car and then told the therapist that he had decided to junk his old car was, in latent language, communicating his suicidal preoccupation to the therapist. When the therapist understood and responded, "Even though you are having a lot of trouble, you might be overlooking the fact that the old car is very useful to you and is worth fixing up," the patient was able to lift the communication out of the metaphor and to state, "I guess there's hope for me, too. Maybe I can get along better when I get fixed up in therapy."

All of the interchanges in regard to time, missed appointments, scheduling of appointments, insisting on promptness, and not changing appointments should be seen as forms of interaction that are designed to reinforce the therapeutic intent and to assure the patient that he is wanted, that therapy is valuable, and that the future is open.

The decision as to the length of the interview depends on many factors. Whether the specific interview is conducted for a fifteen-minute period or for the traditional fifty-minute hour depends on the time available for therapy, the sophistication of the patient, and the ability of the patient to use the time. In some clinics the necessity for fifteen-minute interviews is dictated by the patient load and the limitations of staff time. In programs where the fifteen-minute interview has been used routinely, it has become apparent that even so short a contact can be effective in providing supportive care. On the other hand, some patients who live in a subculture in which psychotherapy and psychoanalysis have become the model for the only "real" treatment must be seen for forty-five or fifty minutes in order to save their self-esteem. These patients are seen for fifty minutes in order to communicate to them that they are getting "first-class treatment" that is "just like psychoanalysis." With the patient who has accepted the values of the psychoanalytic subculture, it is of little value to explain the fact that supportive care is the treatment of choice for his condition and that if he were to be treated by psychoanalysis he would get worse and become increasingly malfunctioning. Patients frequently cannot accept this correct explanation for the choice of treatment.

The planned length of the interview is one aspect of the structure of treatment. It is necessary, therefore, to begin the therapy hour on time. For many patients who come for supportive care, the time spent in therapy is the high point of their life experience during the 168-hour week. They plan every minute of it, and many bring in a well-worked-out agenda. To some patients the therapeutic contact is the only contact with reality during the entire week, and it may be their only real and significant human contact. It is, therefore, highly valued, highly emotionally charged, and overendowed with significance. If, because of inattention, or because of interest in the material presented, or simply because the therapist has extra time and wants to give it to the patient, the appointment is prolonged, the structure is compromised. Staying overtime may imply to the patient that he has become worse, that the structure of the therapy is not controlled, that more is demanded of him, or that the therapist perhaps can be seduced and sidetracked from the therapeutic purpose of the interview. In the neurotic patient who is engaged in expressive psychotherapy, all of these misinterpretations are simply grist for the therapeutic mill and can be interpreted. With the psychotic patient who is receiving supportive care, however, interpretations do not lead to significant insight. To the chronic psychotic patient the behavior of his therapist is as important as anything he says. It is for this reason that infinite attention must be paid to these apparently relatively unimportant details of behavior in the transaction.

The individual interview must be conducted somewhat differently in each meeting with each patient, depending on the amount of integrating adaptive capacity the patient presents at the time of the encounter. As in all interviews, it is best to begin by listening. The "golden three minutes," the overture, if carefully listened to by the therapist, will give him clues as to what will be elaborated during the hour and what the real concerns of the patient are at the time. In order to begin an interview in a nonstructured and open-ended manner, however, the patient must have some adaptive capacity (ego strength). He must be able to respond to the question, "How are things going?" in a coherent enough manner to present the concerns of the week. With some severely malfunctional patients who need a great deal of structure, such an opening is not possible. It may be necessary to conduct a question-and-answer type of interview. In such an interview the therapist must provide many clues to the patient, and in essence he then hears only echoes of himself within the trans-action. A patient who feels so empty and who is so unable to pay attention to his own inner cues requires such reassuring signals from the therapist. In the act of listening to the patient talking about his concerns during the interval between interviews, the therapist responds with three basic communications. First of all, he reassures the patient that he is doing what is expected of him in the therapeutic transaction and that he can feel free to talk about anything he wishes. On the other hand, the therapist selectively responds to and emphasizes the activities reported by the patient. He generally passes over thoughts, wishes, fantasies, delusions, and hallucinations. The purpose of emphasizing action is to reinforce the basic idea that the patient is responsible for what he does. Furthermore, it helps him to differentiate between external reality and internal thoughts and wishes. Chronic psychotic patients have difficulty in making this differentiation. Second, the patient who is listened to by the therapist is shown respect and concern without being judged. That does not mean that the therapist makes no medical judgment. On the contrary, in the medical sense the therapist makes the judgment that reality and activity are important and that certain things the patient does are not in his best interest. Third, the patient is reassured that he may talk about anything he wishes and that, although the therapist believes that certain aspects of his life are more important than others, all feelings and thoughts can be talked about.

Interpretations of content are managed very differently in supportive care than in expressive psychotherapy. They are used much less often, and, if used, an interpretation has a very different therapeutic goal. Interpretation, viewed from a phenomenological point of view, involves some of the following processes. Essentially the patient brings us thoughts, dreams, or behavior that he misunderstands or cannot understand. In the process of interpreting we then say to the patient, in effect, "If you look at this material in such-and-such a way, it seems to me that it makes sense." The process of interpreting has a number of effects in the therapeutic relationship. The healthy neurotic patient's acceptance of an interpretation may lead to a new understanding that subsequently results in a reorganization of his view of himself or of the world. His understanding, it is hoped, then leads to a change in his basic psychological organization. This kind of postulated reorganization does not occur in the chronic schizophrenic patient. He too, however, can benefit from the effects of interpretation. Even though the schizophrenic patient cannot use the interpretation or the understanding in an operational way in order to bring about a change in his adaptational capacities, he can use it to bind anxiety. The patient brings to the therapist thoughts, fantasies, or dreams that he does not understand and about which he is anxious and frightened. The therapist then interprets this material and says, "All of this fits together, and we can understand what these thoughts mean." Whether the interpretation is correct or not has relatively little importance for this aspect of anxiety-binding. The patient can take the interpretation and use it for labeling his frightening or confusing thoughts. In this way he encapsulates the disturbing material and binds the anxiety. If, for example, a patient receiving supportive care brings us a dream, we might simply summarize the manifest content in the interpretation in order to give the patient an anxiety-binding device. We might state, "This dream shows us how much you're concerned with your relationship to your wife." Such an interpretation does not deal with the postulated unconscious material revealed in the latent content. With some patients who are severely disturbed and whose reality-testing is severely impaired, the therapist may interpret a dream purely on a physiological level, as a disturbance of sleep or digestion, or may simply reflect to the patient that "Sometimes some funny things happen in dreams." If the patient is becoming involved in a business venture that is considerably beyond his capacity, an interpretation by the therapist that his attempt represents his "interest in competing with his father" may keep him from getting involved in a venture that will surely fail. Or the patient who acts out in antisocial ways, such as having fights, may respond to an interpretation by the therapist as if the interpretation were in fact a prohibition. Such alterations of behavior resulting from interpretation do not occur because the patient develops insight. Rather, they occur because the patient who is so much in need of the therapist's approval hears every interpretation as a command. When the therapist says, "You get into so many fights because you seem to have a need to prove that you are a man," this patient hears, "You get into so many fights because you seem to have a need to prove that you're a man, and you should not behave in this way."

Because all patients hold the therapeutic encounter in a position of high value, and because the chronic patient who is receiving supportive care often has this encounter as the only source of his self-esteem or as his only human contact, he has great need to please the therapist. Most patients receiving supportive care will pay almost any price in effort or behavior to get approval and the assurance of a continued relationship with the therapist. Since patients are extremely sensitive to the therapist's need and demands, they frequently perceive his wish that the patient should improve. This wish, which is based on the personal needs of the therapist, can lead the patient into interpersonal transactions, business or social, that are considerably beyond his capacity and that are doomed to failure. If the therapist does not recognize what his patient is doing, and if he encourages the patient to try to do what is impossible for him, the patient will fail. Such a failure frequently leads the patient to drop out of the therapeutic situation and therefore to deny himself the support that he so desperately needs. Once the therapist recognizes such maneuvers by the patient, he can "get him off the hook." This result is best produced by recognizing the patient's intent while at the same time conveying to him that he does not need to do this thing in order to please the therapist. If the therapist can give the patient a reward for his effort by stating, for example, "I certainly think it is a good idea for you to think along the lines of getting a job," but at the same time can give the patient permission to fail—"But, after all, you've been ill for a long time and maybe it is still a little too early to think about getting this job"—the therapeutic relationship can be saved. If the patient does not feel the need to perform in order to please the therapist and to maintain the therapeutic relationship, he can function much better in his life situation. That does not mean that we discourage patients from improving their functioning. On the contrary, we attempt to get a patient to function adequately within his capacity at all times. It is only that we do not allow the full force of the positive and dependent transference to push the patient into commitments beyond his capacities and thus into a failure. Most chronic patients find that failure, especially in relation to the therapeutic transaction, has a disastrous effect on their view of the open future. An apparently minor failure, if seen by the patient as representing a closure of his future, can lead to serious disintegration of functioning and even to suicidal attempts.

Reassurance is given throughout the interview. The very fact that the doctor sees the patient, looks after him, and accepts therapeutic responsibility is, in effect, reassuring. At times, however, specific reassurance is necessary, and is an integral part of the process that goes on between the patient and the doctor. The process, however, is not related only to the words that are spoken. Skillful handling of the reassuring aspects of the interview will enhance the therapist's ability to comfort the patient and to alleviate symptoms. Essentially, the physician's reassuring behavior in the interview can be summarized in the statement, "I hear you, I understand you, I accept you, I do not make moral judgments about you. We will collaborate in the effort of understanding your difficulties." Of course, we do not make such statements to the patients literally. Instead, we translate these statements into the practical terms of the transaction, which can be done by a simple confrontation such as, "I guess you're frightened of starting the new job," or, "You seem to feel like crying when you talk about your loneliness." Such statements imply three things: first, that the physician is aware of the patient's fear of emotional upheaval and that the patient is communicating this fear effectively; second, that the physician does not criticize or belittle the patient for having feelings of fear or doubt and that he does not demand that his patient be brave or secure; and third, that the physician will listen if the patient wishes to talk about his sadness or his fear. Obviously such a statement as, "Now, now, don't cry," or, "There is really no reason for you to be afraid," would not communicate reassurance. In fact, it would imply that the physician does not hear, cannot understand, and will not accept such feelings.

The ending of an interview should be as carefully planned as the beginning. As previously mentioned, the ending should fall within the time structure in order to reinforce the security of a realistic and well-planned contact. How the ending is carried out is in part determined by the needs of the patient. For some patients it is reassuring and supportive to receive a short summary of what the therapist has considered a significant aspect of the verbal communication. For example, the therapist might say, "Today we've discussed some of the problems you're having in finding the kind of job you want." To some patients one might give homework with which the patient can bind his anxiety until the next appointment. We might ask a sick patient who has used obsessive defenses in the past to keep careful track of certain feelings or happenings by writing them down and noting the time when they occurred and how long they persisted. With another patient, one might encourage him to explore a certain difficulty before coming for the next appointment, so that he can prepare an agenda for the next interview. With still other patients who are more severely disorganized one might even prescribe specific activities, as, for example, "I think it is important for you to shop in the grocery store at least three times a week, so that we can better understand the difficulties you're having in making choices." Whatever technique is used, at the end of each "hour" the open future must be reinforced, perhaps by a statement like: "We certainly need to discuss this more in your next appointment and to think some more about this problem." The patient must not be placed in the position of leaving the interview with the feeling that he is expected to have solved his problem and that now he must handle it on his own.

For most patients it is only necessary to give the assurance that a future appointment is forthcoming. Patients in need of supportive care generally do not respond well to a vague appointment in the future. Although it may seem medically appropriate to say to a patient, "Call me in three or four weeks to set up another appointment," this statement does not carry the definiteness and the concern and the interest that the patient needs. If the patient can be told to be in the office at precisely 4:15 P.M. on a specific date, this appointment serves the purpose of reassuring him that a time has been set aside for him and that if he does not appear someone will miss him. It further assures him that his therapy is valued highly enough by the physician to be scheduled and that the physician is concerned about him. Some severely disorganized patients need appointment slips. These patients carry a slip with them as though it were a talisman warding off sickness, chaos, or death. When these patients become confused and disorganized, they actually look at the appointment slip during the interim to regain some touch with reality. It is not uncommon for such a patient to call the doctor's office between appointments, ostensibly to check on the time of the next appointment, but really as a means of reminding himself of the reality of this important relationship.

In the structure of the therapeutic encounter between the physician and the patient are found all of the elements necessary for supportive care. In this chapter we have emphasized the importance of the process rather than the content of the interview. It is apparent that the details of the physician's behavior, as well as his verbalizations, are important in conveying interest and concern to the patient. In the supportive interview the emphasis is on reality, activity, and structure, on keeping the future open and reassuring the patient.

11

*Drugs
in the Treatment
of Patients*

--------------------------------------◆
--------------------------------------◆
--------------------------------------◆

Since antiquity drugs have been administered to patients
by physicians and by other representatives of the helping
situation. Drugs have been used to alleviate discomfort, to
alter the state of pathology, to bring about changes in consciousness, to poison or revive, to alter development, or to
change behavior. In the treatment of patients with psychological disturbances, there are a number of psychopharmacological agents that are used to influence behavior in a
systematic way. The primary purpose of these drugs is to alter
the interaction between the patient and his environment. The
effect of the medication on the patient is determined only in
part by the chemistry of the drug. It is also determined by
such factors as the relationship between the therapist who
gives the drug and the patient who receives it and by the

particular dynamics and mechanisms of the symptom that is to be altered. Obviously, response to drugs is highly idiosyncratic. In fact, although drugs can generally be classified by their over-all effect, it is difficult to find a clinically useful classification based on response alone. How the particular drug intervention will work with a given patient at a given time is determined by all of the variables listed above and many more to be discussed in this chapter.

PSYCHOLOGICAL FACTORS IN DRUG MANAGEMENT

The patient's own past history in his relation to drug therapy will necessarily be an important factor in his response to medication. The individual patient who has adopted as part of his life style the chemical intervention—the patient who easily reaches for the aspirin bottle to relieve his headache or the laxative bottle to relieve his difficulty with constipation—will also be ready to seek a pill to alter his feelings and behavior. In many ways this kind of intervention is a passive, magical, and distant one. The patient takes something into his mouth that produces changes inside him, changes that he cannot control, cannot see, and does not understand. Through a complex biological change his behavior is altered in a way that he and the world may judge as more adaptive. The patient has very little part in changing the behavior, nor has he much control over the change. The use of medication reinforces his passivity, allowing him to let the therapist take over in the administration of his destiny. For some patients who feel helpless and overwhelmed by their inner world or by external reality and the demands of interaction with others, this passive approach to problem-solving is seen as control from outside, and for such patients drugs can be therapeutic. For example, for patients who come into the hospital because they feel as if they were sitting on a volcano about to erupt, the introduction of drugs into the treatment is seen as a chemical restraint. Purely from a psychological point of view, in terms of this formulation, anxiety is lessened considerably. On the other hand, the patient who comes to the treatment with a tendency to feel a loss of control over his own life—for example, the paranoid patient—will react very differently to a chemical intervention. He sees the world as influencing him and allowing him no freedom, and he lives in a situation in which mysterious influences alter his behavior from without. He may see chemical intervention as a further attempt to subject him to external control and feel an even greater loss of his own autonomy. Many patients who see the chemical intervention in this way refuse medication, secretly do not take it, or, indeed, discover that the drug further impairs their ability to function.

For other patients medication becomes a representation of the psychological component of the interaction and represents "being given to." For the patient who is deprived, isolated, and unable to make human contact, the administration of a pill may represent the only impingement of the outside world on the prison cell of his psychotic world. When the patient takes medication three times a day, it is at these three times each day that he has contact with reality. This contact may be the only means through which he can perceive, however dimly, that others are concerned or interested or that they care. Being given a pill and swallowing it may be the most significant contact with reality each day. The giving and taking of medication is a highly structured contact. The purpose of the contact is known to both parties involved, and the expectations are simple. The nurse gives the pill and expects the patient to take it. The patient takes the pill from the nurse, who is a representative of the helping situation, and he expects that it will work in some mysterious way to alter his feelings to a more comfortable state. We should remember, however, that for some patients being given a pill may have undesirable effects; for example, a paranoid patient who is certain that he is about to be poisoned will naturally refuse the pill. If he is forced to take a pill, it will confirm his suspicion that others are trying to poison him. Similarly, the psychotically disturbed patient who is depressed may see a pill as something he does not deserve—that it is too much for him to be given such a medical gift—or he, too, may see it as a poison, but may welcome the poison because he sees himself as deserving of being killed. Thus it becomes apparent that the pharmacological reaction of a particular drug in a specific patient at a specific time can be predicted only when one knows a great many facts about the dynamics of the patient to whom the medication is being administered. The great variability in such dynamics makes drug research so difficult that at times it appears that all responses to medication are idiosyncratic.

For many a patient medication serves as a talisman of health, as a sign of good luck, or as a symbolic incarnation of the physician or of the helping situation that wards off the evil forces that make him uncomfortable. For some patients it is apparently not even necessary to take medication; they merely carry it. The fact that the medication is available seems to give security to those who continually feel the threat of an impending loss of control. We have seen patients who take several tranquilizing pills in a medication vial everywhere they go. They never ingest the medication, because they "don't need it"; however, these patients feel secure in the thought that if they do need help at some time when the physician is not readily available, taking a pill will help them until they can get back to the medical transaction. It is a kind of security mechanism by which patients reassure themselves. The sound of the pills rattling in the medication vial while walking can with each step reassure the patient about the reality of the helping situation. Such patients may come to the therapist's office once every three or four months for their supportive appointment in order to have the pills replaced because the external coating is worn off and thus some of the psychological effect has "worn off." What the patient believes about the medication to a very large extent determines how he will respond to it. One of the factors influencing his belief is the physician's belief and how it is conveyed to the patient. If the physician really feels that the medication is helpful in controlling the patient's behavior or feelings, and if he conveys this belief either directly or indirectly to the patient, the psychological effectiveness of the medication is much enhanced.

It is difficult to assess a patient's response to medication when many other treatment interventions are being performed at the same time. For example, if the physician administers medication to a patient on the first visit, one cannot attribute a subsequent change in behavior to the medication. The change may be due entirely to the beginning of the interaction in the helping situation. Thus when one makes it a practice not to administer medication during the first visit or the first few hours of hospitalization, the number of patients requiring medication is markedly reduced. Many patients respond with a major change of behavior toward adaptation and tranquility simply as the consequence of becoming engaged in an interaction with the helping situation.

There are, of course, other patients who are so disorganized in their perception of the world and in their behavioral interaction with it that a chemical intervention is necessary. This chemical intervention may work either by lessening the awareness of anxiety or by allowing the interaction to proceed on a more chemical and therefore somewhat more impersonal level. When the therapist delays the administration of drugs until the second outpatient visit or until the second day of hospitalization, the amount of medication used has been found to be decreased by 70 to 85 per cent. To administer as little medication as possible is not only of value from an economic point of view and from a physiological point of view in terms of avoiding unnecessary side effects; one must also remember that the psychological factors, too, can be antitherapeutic. The administration of medication may further reinforce feelings of helplessness and passivity in the patient. The medication may again convince him that he has no stake in controlling his own destiny. It may reinforce his tendency to look for magical answers to his problems and thus may support a stereotyped, distant approach to the external world in his interpersonal relationships.

Interfering with the Symptom

The major purpose of administering medication is to interfere with symptoms that, in turn, are interfering with the patient's comfort or with his ability to adapt to his surroundings. As is true with any interference with a symptom, however, one must first carefully assess the meaning of and the need for this symptom. Just as it is dangerous to remove a symptom by hypnotic intervention, so it may be potentially dangerous to remove a symptom by other medical interventions. The symptom may be the last adaptive maneuver available to the patient, and its removal may result in partial or even total disorganization of personality. For example, if the patient is frightened to death of being overwhelmed by his angry, aggressive impulses and literally feels that if he lets loose he may murder someone, he may then develop catatonic symptoms. He spends virtually all of his energy in holding his body tight to prevent any of this potentially fatal anger from leaking out. If such a patient is given a chemical agent to loosen his control, the effect might well be antitherapeutic. The medication may have been given with the intent of lessening the patient's anxiety and thus of lessening his need for control; however, it may in fact lessen his ability to control himself. Giving a tranquilizer to such a patient may result in the appearance of overt, wildly psychotic and very destructive behavior that is frightening to the patient and to the environment and may require such physical interventions as restraint. Such an effect of medication has been called paradoxical; however, it is not paradoxical at all if one remembers that the effect of a drug is the *sum* of its chemical and psychological impacts on the patient and his environment. We must remind ourselves that the response to a drug is markedly altered by the meaning of the particular symptom and by the total economics of the psychological make-up of the patient. The therapist must consider that symptoms are formed in response to stresses, either external or internal in nature, and that they thus serve a function. If a symptom is removed chemically, there must necessarily be a shift in the homeostasis or adjustment of the patient. The purpose of the chemical intervention is to shift the adaptive capacity to one of better function. Since symptoms are restitutive in nature, however, this shift to a more adaptive state occurs only if the medication or the intervention alters something besides the symptom.

PHARMACOLOGICAL FACTORS IN DRUG MANAGEMENT

Having considered the psychological factors in the administration of medication, let us now turn our attention to specific pharmacological effects and methods of administration. The first and certainly the most important groups of drugs used in psychiatry are the calming medications. They have been used for a long time. The bromides, the barbiturates, and the opiates are old friends of the physician; they have a long history of helping to calm disturbed behavior. In general these drugs have been abandoned in favor of modern tranquilizers because they tend to be addicting and habituating and to cloud the sensorium.

In the early 1950's a drug derived from the East Indian snake root (Rauwolfia serpentina) was rediscovered for medicine. This drug, which is a derivative of the rauwolfia alkaloid, and which has been marketed as variations of reserpine, was the first major tranquilizer introduced to medicine and thus heralded an era which saw the coming of the term "psychopharmacology." The initial results were startling. Patients who had been disturbed for many years and who had required prolonged hospitalization seemed to respond to fairly large doses of reserpine by calming down and finding it more possible to manage their behavior. Dosages of this drug were ten to one hundred times as large as the dosages used by internists for the control of hypertension. The side effects were many, including hypotension and severe depression. Much experience was gained with this drug in psychiatry during the next few years, and subsequently its use has been abandoned because the side effects are many and the useful effects have been duplicated by other drugs. Today, reserpine, when used by nonpsychiatrist physicians for the control of hypertension, can still be seen to cause depression. This side effect can easily be controlled by discontinuing the drug.

Shortly after the discovery of reserpine, the phenothiazine compounds were discovered. The most important, best known, and most thoroughly studied of these is chlorpromazine (Thorazine). The phenothiazines are derivatives of the antihistamine drugs and have a tendency to calm patients and to control the behavioral sequelae of anxiety and psychotic disorganization. The literature is replete with reports of the advantages of one phenothiazine over another. In point of fact, most of the phenothiazines seem to be about equally effective when given in equivalent dosages. Yet, on occasion, there is important individual variation among patients, so that it is worth while for the physician to be thoroughly familiar with a number of these drugs. In general, the drugs that have been most thoroughly explored are chlorpromazine (Thorazine), prochlorperazine (Compazine), and trifluoperazine (Stelazine). The dosages of these drugs are related as follows: 100 mg. of chlorpromazine is equivalent to 25 mg. of prochlorperazine which, in general, is equivalent to 5 mg. of trifluoperazine. As mentioned previously, patients' responses to the pharmacological effect of drugs are idiosyncratic. As a general guide, an adequate beginning dose for psychotically disturbed patients would be 50 to 100 mg. of chlorpromazine, four times a day. If no major side effects develop, the dosage can be slowly increased until the patient develops the desired calming effect. A rapid change from one tranquilizer to another is of no advantage, since the desired effect often does not appear for several days after administration of the drug is begun. The dosage of chlorpromazine can be safely increased to very large amounts. There are reports in the literature where 4,000 to 5,000 mg. of chlorpromazine daily have been administered for prolonged periods of time to severely disorganized, hospitalized patients. In our experience a patient who does not respond to 800 to 1,000 mg. a day should usually be switched to another phenothiazine in an attempt to gain control of the disturbed behavior at a lower level of dosage. Recently, attempts have been made to combine a number of phenothiazines. The early reports indicate that occasionally, for some patients, there is some advantage in this approach. In general, however, using one drug in adequate dosages over a long enough period of time with careful attention to both pharmacological and psychological factors appears to be the best approach in using this group of major tranquilizers.

The side effects of the phenothiazines are many. One must remember that these drugs enhance the sensitivity of patients to other sedative drugs. Furthermore, they should be avoided in patients with pulmonary insufficiency, since they may impair sensitivity to oxygen lack and thus increase carbon dioxide retention. Many patients develop a pseudo parkinsonism on high doses of phenothiazines. This side effect can be easily controlled with one of the anti-parkinsonism drugs such as trihexyphenidyl (Artane) or procyclidine (Kemadrin), which permit the patient to remain comfortable and still obtain the benefits from the phenothiazine. Occasionally, some problems with hypotension develop as undesirable side effects. In particular, orthostatic hypotension can be a problem in the early administration of the phenothiazines when they are given intramuscularly. Dyskinesia is the most common kind of parkinsonian symptom; it occurs fairly frequently during the first seventy-two hours of treatment. Akathisia or motor restlessness may appear after the first week of treatment. It is characterized by pacing, shifting of stance, rolling or smacking of the tongue, chewing movements of the jaw, and so on. It is more prevalent in younger patients and in women. Classical parkinsonism appears in approximately 50 per cent of patients on trifluoperazine and in 15 per cent of patients on chlorpromazine, if these drugs are given in large dosages. The treatment of choice for the side effect is the reduction of dosage if possible. If it is not possible, the anti-parkinsonism drugs are effective. Other possible side effects of the phenothiazines include a dermatitis and a skin hypersensitivity to sunlight. This hypersensitivity is seen in approximately 5 per cent of the patients taking these drugs. Jaundice was reported as a frequent complication in the early literature on the use of phenothiazines, but it has now become a very rare occurrence. It affects only 0.1 per cent of the patients on phenothiazines, and usually it is cleared when the patient is taken off the medication. As in all medical interventions, there are occasional reports of agranulocytosis. These complications are rare, however, and are not a major problem in the treatment of patients with phenothiazines. Metabolic effects consisting of weight gain, polyphagia, and polydipsia are frequently seen in patients on large dosages of phenothiazines. Also, the seizure potential in patients is increased with the use of these drugs. A patient who is seizure-prone has a tendency to develop more frequent seizures. On occasion, patients who have no history of seizure will develop a seizure disorder with a typically abnormal electroencephalogram. The phenothiazines do not produce seizures but rather potentiate already existing seizure potentials.

Other Useful Tranquilizers

A group of very useful tranquilizers is the group of antihistamines, which are frequently helpful in relieving anxiety and tension. Drugs such as diphenhydramine (Benadryl) and tripelennamine (Pyribenzamine) are inexpensive, and many patients respond to them very well. They too potentiate the effect of narcotics and have some side effects that may be similar to those of the phenothiazines.

The meprobamate drugs have become widely used in today's society. These drugs have some effectiveness in relieving anxiety and, in combination with other drugs, have been used in the treatment of depression. They have a tendency to be habituating, and severe withdrawal symptoms, including seizures, have been reported. These drugs should be used with much care in persons who have a history of or a tendency toward addiction—drug addicts, alcoholics, and, in fact, most patients with chronic emotional disorders. When the meprobamates are used, a dosage of 400 mg. four times a day should be sufficient to obtain a therapeutic effect.

Chlordiazepoxide (Librium) and diazepam (Valium) have during recent years become important drugs in the management of anxiety. They do not cloud the sensorium and apparently are quite helpful in patients who are anxious but who also have some depression. These drugs do not tend to increase depression, as do the phenothiazines. They too have some habituating qualities, although such habituations are generally not nearly so severe as with the meprobamates. Chlordiazepoxide is used in dosages of 10 to 25 mg., four times a day, up to 800 mg. daily.

Alcohol is one of the oldest tranquilizers known to the medical profession. For many years physicians have advised their elderly patients to take a glass of brandy before retiring. In the past, suggestions have been given to the overly anxious housewife that she should take an occasional glass of port wine to calm her nerves and to put her in better spirits. Many patients place themselves on alcoholic medication, since it is a readily available drug that is taken in social settings with much social endorsement. Like all drugs, however, alcohol is habituating and, if taken over prolonged periods of time, may lead to organic damage that is potentially more severe than the damage resulting from other drugs. Any patient who has chronic emotional problems and who has, therefore, a chronic need for finding a way out of his misery is prone to become habituated to almost any medication offered. If this medication is one that is so readily available and so highly advertised as is alcohol, the process of habituation can lead to much secondary difficulty. Furthermore, the chronic schizophrenic who functions in a borderline fashion when he has all of his adaptive capacity available to him frequently cannot function adequately when some of these controls and adaptive capacities are dissolved in ethanol. We are, therefore, of the opinion that patients do better in the long run on medications obtained in a drugstore on a doctor's prescription than on those obtained in a liquor store. The long-term effects of chlordiazepoxide are much less devastating to the central nervous system and much more easily controlled than are those of alcohol.

Antidepressant Medications

A large group of drugs now frequently used in psychiatry are called antidepressant medications. The oldest of these, occasionally placed in this classification, are the central nervous system stimulants. It should be pointed out that these are not antidepressant drugs; as their name states, they simply stimulate the central nervous system of the patient. This stimulation, on occasion, may give the depressed patient enough energy to carry out the sequel of his depression, namely, suicide. These drugs also have the effect of causing a "rebound" depression when their effect has worn off, thus complicating the picture. In general, the central nervous system stimulants are not of value in the treatment of depression.

A group of drugs called monoamine oxidase inhibitors has been used widely during the last few years in the treatment of depression. The results generally have been disappointing, since the medication is slow-acting and may take up to two or three weeks to bring about a response. Many patients do not respond at all. The theory of the action of these drugs is based on the rationale that the breakdown of monoamines is inhibited, and thus serotonin is accumulated, which is thought to help in lifting the depression. Unfortunately, these drugs have many side effects and are potentially extremely dangerous. Not only do they inhibit the breakdown of serotonin, but they also interfere with the breakdown of other naturally-occurring monoamines. Histamine, norepinephrine, and other naturally occurring substances are accumulated. Furthermore, the drugs potentiate the effects of opiates, atropine derivatives, barbiturates, ganglionic blocking agents, corticosteroids, and other drugs. They enhance the effect of certain diuretic drugs and they sensitize patients to certain topical anesthetics. Psychiatrically, they may produce an unmasking of a basic schizophrenic process and provoke a state of psychokinetic stimulation or a toxic confusional reaction. When they are used in combination with other antidepressant medications or with phenothiazines, they are potentially fatal. The side effects are severe, including dizziness, restlessness, excitability, visual hallucinations, and severe sweating. There have been a number of reports of cardiovascular collapse and death. In view of the limited usefulness of these drugs in alleviating depression and the potentially fatal side effects, the authors do not advocate their use.

The currently available, useful, and fairly safe antidepressants consist of amitriptyline (Elavil) and imipramine (Tofranil), which are atropine-like drugs and which seem to help some patients with symptoms of depression. These drugs are given in dosages of 10 to 20 mg., three or four times a day. If a patient is given an adequate dosage, he may respond within the first three hours or within up to three or four days. If he does not respond within one week, the drug will probably not be effective. The side effects include occasional difficulty with urethral sphincter spasm, which is quickly corrected by discontinuing the medication. Generally speaking, none of the antidepressant drugs available today is highly effective.

BASIC PRINCIPLES OF DRUG ADMINISTRATION

As can be seen from the foregoing discussion, our present psychopharmacological armamentarium is manifestly inadequate. The drugs are nonspecific, have many side effects, and depend to a major extent on the psychological interaction between the helping situation and the patient. In view of these pharmacological circumstances, the primary dictum of the physician ought to be the old saying, "Primum non nocere" (first of all, do no harm). The simplest, safest, and cheapest drug that will help to manage the patient is the medication of choice. We have discovered that many patients, if given enough attention and enough opportunity to interact with a significant human being in the helping situation, do not require medication. If medication is used for its pharmacological effect, however, it is best for the physician to familiarize himself thoroughly with the drug. He should know and recognize all of the side effects and understand their action. If he can use one or two drugs well, he is better able to help his patients than if he uses many drugs with little background and little experience. Many physicians have a tendency to use these drugs in dosages that are too low. If a drug is to be tried, it should be prescribed in an adequate dose—one that is high enough and is administered long enough to have a chance of succeeding. In general, the patient should be maintained on a drug for a period of time to see how it will affect him, without rapid day-to-day or even every-other-day switching from one medication to another. The simplest kind of psychopharmacological approach is the best, using the fewest medications and the lowest dosage that will do the job. For many schizophrenic patients who are maintained chronically on medication, a low maintenance dosage can be determined over a period of months and years by carefully observing the patient. With these patients, too, the lowest dosage of the cheapest drug with the fewest side effects is the treatment of choice.

Much has been written on the placebo effect of medication. In the first section of this chapter we discussed the psychological effect, which, in our opinion, is to be clearly distinguished from the placebo effect. Every medication given by or on order of the physician has an important psychological effect on the patient and on the medical transaction. To call it a placebo effect implies that the patient is being "tricked." If, in fact, the physician is tricking the patient, the transaction generally does not work out well. Beyond all else, the physician must offer an authentic investment in the transaction with the patient. Thus, when physicians talk about the placebo effect and imply that the patient is being tricked, there is potential danger that the lifesaving doctor-patient relationship may be explosively disrupted when the patient discovers the hoax, or when the physician finds it impossible to carry on the deceit. Honesty with patients is necessary. That does not mean that we tell patients all that we know. It does mean that we do not tell patients things that are untrue, that we make the tactical decision of how much of what we know we should convey to the patient, and that this decision should be based on his needs rather than ours.

In a multidisciplinary approach to the treatment of chronic emotionally ill patients, such as chronic schizophrenics who are in need of supportive care, the actual treatment is frequently carried out by a nonphysician therapist. In this situation a number of questions arise regarding the use of medication. The authors have found it advisable to let the therapist, whether he be physician or nonphysician, hand the prescription to the patient. Obviously, the prescription must be written by a licensed physician who knows the case well, who has initially seen the patient, and who follows him medically. In the usual practice the patient will have been seen by the physician once, the medication will be prescribed by him, and on subsequent visits renewal of the prescription by the physician will be requested by the nonphysician therapist. At regular intervals the nonphysician therapist discusses the case with the physician, and also at regular intervals medical precautions are taken, consisting of appropriate laboratory tests and occasional interview contacts between the patient and the prescribing physician. The patient is aware of the role and function of the physician in prescribing the medication, and he is also aware of the role of his own nonphysician therapist in monitoring the treatment transaction with the assistance of the physician. In private practice, a similar kind of transaction can be carried out. The nonphysician therapist can refer the patient to his own family doctor or to some other collaborating physician for the management of medications. It is important that the physician be willing to accept the role of the administrator of the medication through the nonphysician therapist, and that these two representatives of the helping situation cooperate closely. Our experience with this type of coordinated therapeutic effort in institutional settings has been replicated in noninstitutional practice, and our success in utilizing and teaching this method of jointly sharing the responsibility for the treatment of chronically ill patients leads us to conclude that the method represents a useful extension of the therapeutic regimen into an area where there is a great and unmet need.

It has been our experience in managing chronic patients that prescriptions should not be made renewable. More than anything else, these patients need control. Even if the patient must go to a drugstore and have the pharmacist call the physician for renewal, it offers some control and some contact for the patient. To give such a patient a prescription that can be renewed ten or twenty times may be a serious hazard in terms of the patient's confusion, his possible suicidal use of the medication, and his losing contact with the helping situation.

12
Aftercare

◆
◆
◆

Supportive treatment of the chronically ill patient utilizes many techniques and situations over an extended period of time for the purpose of helping the patient to maximize his functioning and minimize his distress. The techniques used and the situation in which they are applied must be chosen on the basis of the patient's needs at the time of the treatment intervention. The decision as to where the patient should be treated and what techniques should be applied must be carefully considered in terms of the therapeutic needs of the patient, the availability of support in the environment, and the patient's history of treatment.

For purposes of discussion we have arbitrarily taken a segment of treatment that is conducted outside of the setting of total hospitalization and that occurs after the patient has been hospitalized and have called it *aftercare*. Similar techniques can be used even if the patient has never been hospitalized, but then we call the treatment *outpatient care*. This distinction between outpatient treatment and aftercare is not only an arbitrary division for purposes of presentation of the material, but it also serves to emphasize that the problems of treatment are altered once the patient has been hospitalized. The history of having been hospitalized produces both unique problems and unique opportunities for treatment. The history of a carefully planned, well-conducted, brief hospitalization can become an important part of the patient's treatment and management in the future. We have already stated (Chapters 7 and 8) our attitude that hospital treatment is a potent intervention that must be judiciously applied after all of the indications and contraindications have been considered in detail. A patient should be hospitalized for the briefest period that allows the fulfillment of the specific therapeutic aim in the prescription of hospitalization for a given patient at a given time in the management of his illness. Hospitalization should be terminated as quickly as possible and other techniques of treatment instituted. These aftercare techniques must supply support, continuity, and confirmation of the therapeutic aim, and most importantly they must allow the patient to take increasing control over his own destiny as he becomes prepared to do so. Thus aftercare is not a specific technique, but rather a variety of treatment interventions that occur after the patient has been in the hospital. The tactics of aftercare must allow for the patient's constantly changing adaptive capacity as he takes increasing control over the conduct of his life in the transition from the hospital treatment to extramural care. Aftercare techniques include outpatient visits of varying lengths for psychotherapy or activity, telephone contacts with a representative of the helping situation, day hospital care, night hospital care, "halfway house" treatment, attachment to nonprofessional support groups, such as Recovery, Inc., and so forth. All of these techniques, when they are used as aftercare, have in common that they call on the meaning of hospitalization as a part of the treatment technique.

After the patient has left the hospital, a number of problems must be dealt with in aftercare that result specifically from the patient's having been hospitalized and from his separation from the hospital. Of course, there are also the many problems that are directly related to the interaction of the patient and his illness with the world in which he has to live. The problems resulting from having been hospitalized, however, are unique for the aftercare transaction and require the attention of the therapist. All hospitalization, by its taking over the conduct of the patient's life, fosters dependency and regression. This dependency and regression need to be undone as the patient is propelled back into the extramural world. Although the problem of dependency is discussed in detail in Chapter 4, we emphasize here that one of the inevitable undesirable side effects of hospitalization is the fostering of dependency. In order to conduct hospital treament successfully, it is necessary for us to care in an almost total way for the patient and thus to place him in a dependent role. This fostering of dependency is not part of the therapeutic intent, but an unavoidable side effect, somewhat analogous to the unavoidable extrapyramidal symptoms seen in patients who receive large dosages of phenothiazines. If one desires the therapeutic effect of large dosages of tranquilizers, one must be prepared to deal with the concomitant side effects by prescribing other medications to help the patient with this iatrogenic problem. Similarly, when we use hospitalization in supportive treatment we must be prepared to deal with the constantly occurring, undesirable side effects of dependency. The patient's first reaction will be to return to the hospital when he has difficulty in his life. He will tend to see it as the most readily available and inviting source of support, so much so that the therapist may find himself in the position of guarding the doors of the hospital to keep the patient out. It is almost as if one were dealing with a patient who had become addicted to a medication. A patient can become addicted to hospitalization as the solution to all problems of living. If he is allowed to give in to his craving, he may become a chronically hospitalized, totally incapacitated human being who resides on a ward of a state hospital for several decades. In aftercare treatment the hospital must be abstracted by the patient with the help of the therapist so as to become a symbol of therapy. The patient must learn to use the idea of hospitalization and at times even to look at the actual hospital building as a resource for support, rather than having to be admitted to the hospital to obtain this support. There are many patients who help themselves with this symbolization of the hospital for support by carrying a picture of the building or by driving by the hospital to reassure themselves that it is still there, that it always will be there, and that if things really get bad it can be an available resource for treatment. The "well-trained" aftercare patient can utilize the symbol of the hospital as the great stone mother and can learn to use this symbolic representation of the helping situation in moments of crisis and panic without actually needing to return for intramural care. Thus one of the major tasks of the aftercare therapist is to convert the actual experience of treatment in the hospital into a symbolic representation of the hospital as a source of treatment.

There are some secondary social complications that may result from a patient's hospitalization. Some of these have been discussed in Chapter 7, "The Decision for Hospitalization." In the aftercare situation some of these social problems may at times become major issues. For example, the family of the patient or the other supporting resources may also have to be weaned away from the attitude that the hospital is to be used as the only resource every time the patient becomes upset or disturbed. Once hospitalization has been introduced into the patient's history of treatment, his family and supporting resources tend to overuse this technique. In fact, at times the family or supporting agency may use the threat of rehospitalization as a device to make the patient comply with all demands. The therapist must help the family or agency to avoid this antitherapeutic use of the idea of hospitalization. He must help them to understand the difference between saying to the patient, "If you don't come home for dinner tonight, we will have to take you back to the hospital," and "If you and your doctor agree that further hospitalization is of value at this time, we will help you to get to the hospital."

To our readers who are experienced therapists in a hospital

setting, it must be clear from their work in the admitting room that a patient who has a "history of previous hospitalization" is greeted with a very different attitude than is someone for whom his admission represents the first hospital intervention. A history of previous hospitalization seems to result in ready admission to the hospital, a more pessimistic view of the prognosis, and a tendency to keep the patient in the hospital for longer periods of time than are therapeutically indicated. To decide that a patient who has a history of previous hospitalization has a poorer prognosis is to make a self-fulfilling prophecy. None of these attitudes is justified by fact or observation, especially when hospitalization is seen as a brief period of a special kind of treatment in the long-term care of a chronically ill patient.

Specific problems occur as the result of leaving the hospital that must be dealt with in the early phases of aftercare. These problems are the result of the separation panic that the patient experiences as he is guided from intramural to extramural care at the time of discharge. The vast majority of patients have a history of a major campaign to maintain themselves in homeostasis outside of the hospital prior to admission. Thus when the decision for hospitalization is finally made, one of the common side effects is a feeling of failure and defeat in the patient and at times in the therapist. As the patient later leaves the hospital, we ask him to go back to the same battleground on which he has experienced defeat. Once again, albeit with new resources and after a period of rest, he has to attempt the battle of his life space. As we send him back on the firing line, he has to deal with his history of having been previously defeated. He requires support in the handling of his anxiety. Many patients and therapists prolong hospitalization to avoid facing this anxiety, thereby compounding the difficulty of leaving the hospital. These problems arising as the result of separation from the hospital must be turned about through the skillful use of the supportive relationship with the therapist, in order to make it possible to utilize the symbol of the hospital and the history of the hospitalization as a built-in therapeutic device for the future benefit of the patient. Frequently the patient wishes or even demands to return to the hospital as he faces his adaptive task in life. It is at this point that the therapist must be so well in charge of the ever-changing situation that he can withhold hospitalization long enough to allow for development of the symbolic representation of the hospital as a therapeutic agent, without rejecting the patient or withdrawing the use of the hospital as a possibility for treatment. In our experience only 20 per cent of the patients who leave the hospital need further hospital treatment in the following two years.

The problems of the transition from the hospital into the extramural world can be minimized when the same therapist can continue to offer the supportive care. Even a change of therapist can be tolerated by patients, however, if it is handled with adequate preparation by the hospital therapist. For the neurotic patient who is receiving expressive therapy, changing therapists is fraught with difficulty; the more severely ill patient receiving supportive care can make this change more easily. His transference is more diffusely attached to the therapeutic situation rather than to a specific person. In some clinics the therapist may even change for each aftercare appointment. Although that is not the best procedure, it has been found workable if necessary. If a change in therapist has to be made as the patient moves to extramural care, the effect can be minimized by having the transition occur in the locale of the hospital. For example, if an aftercare patient can be seen for his outpatient visits in the hospital from which he was discharged or even on the ward in which he received his hospital treatment, the full force of the history of hospitalization can be utilized in a concrete way in forging the symbolic representation of the hospital as treatment.

The most common form of aftercare is outpatient treatment conducted after the patient has left the hospital. The patient returns on a regular basis, usually once a week or once every two weeks, for a short period of time to discuss his concerns and progress. Although a great deal of emphasis is placed on the patient's increasing adaptive capacity in dealing with his life problems, it must be stated once again that this emphasis on and expectancy for change must not be portrayed, communicated, or even felt by the therapist as a demand that the patient function at a level beyond his capacity. As described in Chapter 10, "Management of the Therapy 'Hour,'" the major emphasis in both the verbal and the nonverbal transaction during the outpatient visit must be on reality and activity. It must serve to keep the future open and to re-emphasize the continuity of the supporting relationship. The aftercare visits may be brief. In many settings, including those in our own experience, a fifteen-minute interview once a month may eventually be sufficient to maintain the kind of supportive relationship necessary to help the patient to function when the crisis that led to his hospitalization has passed. How frequently the patient should be seen and how long interviews should be need to be determined by the realistic, therapeutic requirements of the patient. Unfortunately, however, the length and frequency of aftercare visits is often determined by the administrative routine in a particular clinic. Such routines often inappropriately mimic classical psychoanalysis by insisting on fifty-minute appointments several times a week. Still other clinic routines are determined by the convenience of making out schedules, resulting in a patient's making weekly visits when only one visit a month or every two weeks is indicated.

The frequency and length of the visits should be changed in the course of aftercare with the patient's changing needs for support. One must recognize, however, that problems will result if a change in frequency or length of visit is misinterpreted by the patient. That does not mean that one cannot make changes; rather it means that their side effects must be dealt with in the therapeutic transaction. The patient is likely to interpret a decrease in the frequency or length of visits as progress toward termination. Some patients even interpret such

a decrease as a signal from the therapist that they are not performing adequately or that they are boring him. Such fantasied
rejection cannot be tolerated by the sort of patient whose need
is for supportive care. On the other hand, an increase in the
frequency or length of visits that the therapist introduces because he feels that the patient is making progress and can thus
utilize more intensive care may in fact be misinterpreted by
the patient as a signal that the therapist feels he is becoming
sicker or more disorganized. Either of these misinterpretations
can be handled by a thorough discussion and a fairly long
period of preparation before introducing a change.

Generally, aftercare therapy has been provided by many
representatives of the helping situation. Traditionally, psychiatrists, psychologists, and social workers have functioned in
aftercare clinics. The authors have experimented with the use
of nonprofessional aftercare therapists and have found the
results satisfying, both to the patient and to the clinic. We
have used medical students, nursing students, psychiatric
nurses, and psychiatric aides, and we have found them to be
effective, supportive therapists in aftercare if properly supervised and instructed.

The use of telephone contacts with the patient may be of
great value in making the transition from the hospital to the
extramural world, and in making the transition from more
frequent to less frequent aftercare visits. The technique consists of a regularly appointed time during which the therapist
may call the patient, or vice versa, and talk for perhaps five
minutes to allow the patient to "check in." The therapist can
use the telephone contact to "take the pulse" of the patient, in
order to monitor more accurately the patient's transition into
the outside world. The telephone contact for support in the
aftercare situation, which requires a minimum expenditure of
time on the therapist's part, must utilize all of the basic principles of treatment of the chronically ill. It must be consistent
and reliable, it must keep the future open by planning for the
future, and it must allow the patient a dependency which does

not inhibit his ability to function any more than is necessary. As the patient improves in his adaptive capacity, he may take responsibility for initiating the telephone call rather than having the therapist call him. Obviously, the kind of telephone contact initiated by "Call me at any time between now and your next appointment, if you need me," is much less supportive in a carefully planned program of aftercare than a telephone appointment made by saying, "Until I see you again next month on May 27, I would like to talk to you once a week each Friday morning at 8:00 A.M. I will call you at those times, and I expect you to be at your telephone and to keep the line open so that we may have a five-minute conversation about your situation." The former requires the patient to initiate the contact and requires that the patient decide whether the therapist really wants him to call or not. The latter is a situation that is planned, initiated by the therapist, taken seriously by both patient and therapist, and is a part of the expectancy of the situation. It keeps the future open because specified times at future dates are set aside for this specific transaction between the patient and the therapist, and the responsibility for the treatment is taken by the therapist rather than the patient.

Another variant of outpatient treatment in aftercare is the use of activities. Recently, some therapists have experimented with the use of outpatient occupational and activity treatment. Especially with a patient who began an interest in an activity while in the hospital, and who used this activity as an important aspect of treatment, outpatient occupational therapy is found to be of value in the transition into the extramural world. The patient who began a mosaic as part of an occupational therapy group project while in the hospital may continue to do this work at home and to bring it back for each appointment to check on his progress and to get help and advice with his task. He may even return to the inpatient occupational therapy group to participate in a day hospital activity. Such a use of activity in aftercare, rather than the traditional talking about the patient's problems with his adaptive task in the extramural world, is most suitable for the sickest and most severely incapacitated patients. Some patients may return to the group therapy meetings in the inpatient setting as a further supportive technique. Others find it possible to use outpatient groups of former hospital patients to obtain their support.

For some patients it seems a useful supportive measure to have them return to the hospital to obtain their medication. Although it may be practical for some patients to take their aftercare prescriptions for medications to outside pharmacies, there are other patients for whom it is important that they obtain the medication from the hospital. For them, receiving the pills at the hospital pharmacy adds a great deal of support and allows them to continue their trusting relationship to the stone mother, the hospital.

We have noted that some patients after being discharged from the hospital continue to use the institution as the center of their life space. Such patients may want to visit other patients in the hospital, to do favors for them, to bring them clothes, and so forth. In the usual administrative structure of the public hospital, such activities are frowned upon. In some private hospitals former patients have been used effectively as adjunctive treatment staff, much to the benefit of the patients remaining in the hospital and of the former patients now functioning as auxiliary therapists. We have seen many patients who obtain a great deal of support and reassurance from being able to do things for other patients. In special cases, with careful planning and excellent supervision, having aftercare patients participate in some suitable service or treatment function for inpatients can be highly therapeutic.

The use of the day hospital or night hospital offers important extensions of the therapeutic armamentarium in the care of the chronically ill. The patient who is not yet ready to make the total transition into the extramural world or whose social support resources are extremely limited may use the hospital on a part-time basis in taking his step to the outside.

The patient who can begin working but who cannot yet function in a difficult family setting or in the loneliness of an apartment may well ensure the success of his extramural adaptive task by the utilization of the night hospital. He can go out each day to work, but in the evening he can return to the hospital to maintain the concrete link with the helping situation. Similarly, the day hospital is of value to many patients. It is suitable for the patient who is able to handle the adaptive task of dealing with his family but who is not yet able to manage a work situation or the discomfort of an idle day. Such a patient comes to the hospital to participate in the regular therapeutic activities, preferably in the situation in which he experienced them as an inpatient. During his day hospital experience he can assure himself that the hospital is a helping situation, that it is available, and that he can make the transition to using the symbolic hospital rather than the concrete hospital as a representative of the helping situation. For some patients it is so difficult to make the transition from intramural to extramural care that they have to be weaned very slowly from total hospitalization. Thus, each week, day hospital care may be decreased by one hour, so that eventually the patient makes the transition from eight hours of hospitalization each day to one hour of hospitalization each day, to one fifteen-minute aftercare visit a week, and eventually to one fifteen-minute aftercare visit a month. When one fifteen-minute aftercare visit a month offers enough support to maintain the patient in adequate functioning, then obviously his adaptive capacity has markedly increased over the time when he needed total hospitalization. This transition at times may go rapidly, in a matter of weeks; at other times it may take years. Yet the issue in aftercare is much the same as in hospitalization. The least amount of treatment that does the job is the best treatment. It does not mean that we do as little as possible or that we give inadequate care in order to save time. It does mean that the therapeutic gains in each phase of supportive care must be clearly defined and that we fulfill these therapeutic aims in such a way as to minimize for the patient the antitherapeutic side effects of treatment.

Another alternative to hospitalization is the use of the "halfway house," which differs from the day hospital or night hospital in that it is not in the physical location in which the patient had his hospital experience. It is by definition halfway between a complete extramural adjustment and complete hospital treatment. Most halfway houses offer a variety of services ranging from total care in the halfway house (which most closely resembles hospitalization) to day care, night care, and outpatient treatment and aftercare. Total care in a halfway house, however, differs from hospital care in that it is not so highly structured, nor is the setting like that of the hospital, in which dependency is so constantly fostered. Many halfway houses also have the advantage of being located in a city, where the patient can more easily make his transition, in contrast to the many psychiatric hospitals that are still located at a considerable distance from population centers.

In this chapter approaches to the aftercare of the patient have been described as part of the total treatment program available for supportive care. Aftercare has been defined as a phase of treatment that occurs after the patient has left the hospital and that relies heavily on human interaction, as does all treatment. It adds to the other forms of supportive care the utilization of the symbolic representation of the hospital as a powerful therapeutic agent. A large portion of aftercare addresses itself to the task of converting the actual experience of having been in the hospital to the symbolic representation of the hospital as a helping situation to be utilized by the patient in future crises and panics.

13

The Suicidal Patient

—————————————————————◆
—————————————————————◆
—————————————————————◆

Many of the chronic patients whose care and treatment are described in this book periodically have suicidal ruminations and make suicide attempts. It is of the greatest importance for the therapist to be able to evaluate these attempts carefully so that he can make the appropriate treatment decisions. Certainly, any suicide attempt or thought must be taken seriously. If nothing else, each suicide attempt is a dramatic call for help. Even the idea that a patient entertains a thought about suicide and considers the possibility of asking for help in such a dramatic and self-destructive way must be dealt with by the therapist.

The statement that each suicidal thought or attempt or gesture must be taken seriously should not, however, be construed as meaning that each one should necessarily result in hospitalization. Certainly, attempted suicides or successful suicides occur, and remind us that we make errors in judgment, but we are not reminded often enough of our errors in judgment in the direction of hospitalizing too soon and too frequently in response to the suicidal risk. If one is as cautious as one ought to be, it is easy to say that it is better to err on the side of hospitalizing a patient who is suicidal than to err on the side of taking a chance with suicide. It is undeniable that a dead patient cannot be treated, but we should also remind ourselves that hospitalization for a chronically ill patient can be detrimental and, in particular, that prolonged hospitalization may lead to lifelong invalidism as secondary to the treatment intervention. We may take little comfort from having prevented a suicide if, at the same time, we have reinforced lifelong nonfunctioning or invalidism in a patient. Even though errors made in not hospitalizing a patient are more dramatic and can be fatal, errors of hospitalizing patients who should not be hospitalized, who do not need to be hospitalized, and for whom hospitalization is grossly antitherapeutic are probably statistically much more frequent and, in the long run for our population of chronic patients, much more harmful.

Often a chronic schizophrenic patient is seen by a therapist after a suicidal attempt. Some differentiation needs to be made between a gesture and an attempt. Generally, it is assumed that a patient has engaged in a suicidal gesture when the primary purpose of the act is to manipulate persons or objects in the environment. One should not make the mistake of thinking that suicidal gestures are therefore not dangerous. They can be exceedingly dangerous, although if they are fatal they usually are accidentally so. A typical example of such an "accidental suicide" is the patient who is angry at someone significant in his or her environment and who, in acting out this anger, takes an overdose of sleeping pills at a certain time, expecting to be discovered. On that particular day the person who was to have made the discovery stops at the local tavern and does not return for several hours. As a consequence, the patient dies. It is this kind of suicidal gesture that can turn out to be fatal.

As distinct from the gesture, the suicidal attempt is involved when death plays a part in the motivational system. Dr. Karl Menninger devised a way of looking at the suicidal attempt. He felt that each suicidal attempt contains a sadistic, a masochistic, and a withdrawal element or, to put it in more popular terms, it includes the killing, the being killed, and the dying. Which one of these aspects predominates gives us some important diagnostic clues about the patient and also some help in making prognoses about future attempts. Rather typically, when a schizophrenic patient makes a suicidal attempt one finds that the killing (sadism) predominates. If he survives the attempt, the patient frequently is able to say that he did not want to die, that he did not want to be killed, but that he wanted to kill the bad part, the ineffective part of himself. He wanted to kill the introject. On occasion a schizophrenic will say after a suicide attempt that he did not realize that he would die in the attempt to rid himself of the "bad self." This kind of suicide is usually very violent and sadistic. These are the people who swan-dive off a bridge into a freeway, who blow out their brains, who run into an airplane propeller or an oncoming train to get themselves chopped up, or who dive off a twenty-story building to splatter themselves across the sidewalk. These sadistic suicides are highly unpredictable and frequently are not associated with recognizable depression. One can see such a patient for an appointment and two hours later hear of his violent suicide, having had no inkling or whisper of the possibility.

A patient with psychotic depression, usually of a nonschizophrenic type, may demonstrate the predominance of the masochistic element, the "being killed." It is this kind of patient—typified by the involutional depression—who wrings her hands and says, "I am no good. I ought to be killed. I have sinned." She does not want to kill. She does not want to withdraw. She wants to be killed to pay for her sins. These suicides are less dangerous than those previously mentioned in that they are more predictable, more closely related to depression, and can be more easily monitored. When such a patient is becoming more depressed, it is easy to see this in the interview and to take appropriate steps to prevent a suicide.

The last of these suicidal dynamics is withdrawal, seen in the patient who can no longer face his problems, who feels that he would like to go to sleep, never to wake up again. He does not particularly want to kill or to be killed; he just wants to die, to sleep, to wake no more. These suicide attempts are seen primarily in depression of a neurotic type; they are less dangerous, and they are the most easily monitored.

In summary, all aspects of suicide must be taken seriously. The suicidal gesture can be accidentally fatal. The suicidal attempt may be fatal. The most dangerous of the suicidal attempts is the kind associated with schizophrenia, because there is little possibility of monitoring the suicidal intent. All suicidal attempts contain elements of sadism, masochism, and withdrawal; which one of these predominates gives important clues to the danger of future suicidal behavior.

The problem of preventing suicide in the chronic schizophrenic patient is complicated by the fact that the reasons for suicide are not so much the results of specific crises as of a long-term process of which the patient is frequently aware. Many of these patients do not want to kill themselves or to die or to be killed, in terms of our previous discussion. It is rather a question of not wanting to live; as many of these patients become aware of the chronicity of the loneliness, the isolation, and the alienation in which they pass their existence, as they become aware of the feelings of rejection and inauthenticity that they carry away from each human encounter, as they become aware of their emptiness, the futility of their lives becomes obvious to them. It is then that many of them no longer want to live. They do not want to die, to kill themselves, or to be killed, but they do not want to live, to exist in a world in which human contact does not provide them with any lasting feelings. Many chronic schizophrenic patients who are bright and observant, as well as verbally facile, can describe this emptiness and this lack of satisfaction in the human encounter dramatically and poetically. No matter how much love and affection the helping other or the involved other pours into such a patient, no matter how many experiences of success the patient has, no matter how many gratifying "human contacts" are part of his history, none of it seems to become incorporated into his being; so to speak, nothing "sticks to his ribs." He walks through life feeling unloved, unwanted, worthless, and isolated, and in spite of the concern or interest of others, he cannot be convinced that there is hope for something better for him. The problem for the therapist then becomes a difficult one, because he is placed in the position of having to provide reasons why the patient should not commit suicide. This becomes a critical therapeutic task. Such patients not only place the therapist in this position but frequently also various members of the family. A spouse or a parent sometimes accepts the task placed on him by the chronically ill patient of preventing his suicide. He walks on eggs around the patient, tiptoeing consciously in order not to say or do anything that might produce a suicidal threat. Both the therapist and the family member who accepts this uncomfortable and untenable situation finds himself on occasion unconsciously beginning to push the patient into suicide, as if to "get it over with," because this sword of Damocles hanging over his head is unbearable.

The therapist can usually handle this situation for the family by figuratively getting them "off the hook." If someone really wants to commit suicide, there is no sure way to prevent his so doing. How far we go in preventing suicide depends at times on whether we are willing to take certain risks in the clinical situation in order to accomplish what is best for the patient. Obviously, once a patient has committed suicide he is no longer available for treatment, but we must be aware that if we hospitalize a patient or place him in restraints in order to keep him from committing suicide we may, in fact, be doing him more harm than good.

It cannot be stated strongly enough or often enough that if someone really is determined to commit suicide, nothing can prevent him from doing so sooner or later. The therapist's task is not solely to prevent the patient's suicide, but rather to evaluate the pressures and feelings that, at the moment, have come together so that the patient feels that suicide is the only possible alternative. A careful evaluation of these forces will first of all determine whether the condition is temporary. If so, all measures must be taken to keep the patient from committing suicide until a condition is alleviated or the situation has changed. For example, a chronic schizophrenic patient who has recently experienced another rejection from which he feels he cannot bounce back is potentially suicidal. He has just experienced the hurt of once again having demonstrated to himself that he is worthless and unlovable, and he feels that he cannot face making another effort to relate to another human being in order to obtain the kind of satisfaction in a relationship that he knows, or at least suspects, he can never have. At this point the future appears closed to him. With such a patient we must take all measures necessary to keep him from committing suicide, while at the same time providing exposure to a human relationship (usually with the therapist) that offers him an opportunity to seek satisfaction and that thus introduces hope. Once he is again involved in the task of forming a relationship or using a relationship with a fellow human being who is a representative of the helping situation in order to alleviate his distress, it then becomes possible for him to suspect that future relationships are possible. In this way the future is reopened. Hope once more becomes part of his life style, and a fellow human being has been used in order to alleviate distress. Each time the chronic patient can use a relationship to fellow human beings in order to alleviate distress he has a positive experience and comes to recognize the possibility that the next relationship may also be positive. The patient who has a relationship, and who thus has a future, is much less likely to commit suicide.

There are a number of specific interventional principles that can be thought of as measures for preventing suicide. Most important among them is the interruption of the patient's isolation. As has been thoroughly documented in a number of studies, almost every patient who is considering suicide as an alternative to living reaches out for help or at least lets significant others know of his plans. Even the chronic schizophrenic patient who does not show clearly an identifiable concurrent depression has a tendency to signal his consideration of the suicidal act. At this point an interruption of his isolation is lifesaving, and human contact must be provided, if necessary by force. Since, as we have mentioned in other portions of this book, for many of these patients the relationship to the helping situation is diffuse rather than specific to one therapist, many resources can be mobilized. Relatives, neighbors, agencies, officials, hospitals, and physicians are all avenues that can be used to interrupt isolation. Thus, for example, the therapist might call the patient regularly each day or insist that a friend or relative temporarily spend time with the patient or live with him, or it might be suggested that the patient work longer hours or engage in a volunteer activity where there is contact with others. One of many possible interventions might be an insistence that the patient go to the grocery store several times a day for small items, which might be enough to interrupt the isolation and provide the kind of human contact that can prevent suicide. By no means does intervention imply that whoever is with the patient should hover over him or should set up a situation the primary purpose of which is to exercise control. For some patients control is necessary, but for all of them it is the human contact that is of primary importance. It should also be remembered that many of these patients, at the time of their suicidal ruminations as well as at other times, fear close contact or involvement with other human beings. At the same time they fear isolation. Thus whoever is providing the human contact in order to interrupt their isolation must allow the distance between himself and the patient to be dictated by the patient's momentary needs. Many patients see too much closeness as a demand, which can push them into suicide; yet too much distance will not adequately interrupt the isolation. How much closeness and how much distance requires a constant vigilance toward the patient's needs and a thorough separation of the patient's needs from the therapist's needs. When the therapist responds to his own need for closeness, he may frighten the patient into a more suicidal position or into a position of having to give up the lifesaving human contact that interrupts the isolation.

Another important aspect of suicide prevention is the enforcement of activities. Some of the suggestions made in the foregoing paragraph indicate that part of the interruption of isolation includes the enforcement of activity. When the patient is asked to go to the grocery store three times a day to buy at least one item, not only is there interruption of isolation and some provision for human contact as a potential source of help, but there is also insistence on the physical activity of going to the grocery store, selecting and buying something, and returning home. To ask—indeed to insist— that the patient engage in certain activities which are planned to interrupt isolation also tends to get the patient going, reinforces reality, and supports his ego-function to the extent that he is functioning enough to be active. Some minimal resources of self-esteem remain to the patient. Since the activity is performed in a sequence of Aristotelian time with a subliminal recognition of the anticipation, passage, and memory of clock time, the future is thus forcefully kept open. Activity has a tendency to prevent hopelessness and circular ruminations. As long as the patient can be helped to remain active even at the most primitive level, hope remains in the situation, and hope, of course, is the best suicide preventive.

It is impossible for a patient to engage in any kind of activity that frequently brings him out of his isolation without developing at least a suspicion that life can be different, can even be better, and that suicide is not the only alternative to living with his pain, agony, and alienation.

A third treatment intervention that is frequently helpful is making plans for the future with the patient. The therapist cannot plan the patient's future for him, but he can insist on a collaborative approach to planning. The patient should make plans, or at least consider the possibility of plans, with the assistance of the therapist. To the extent that the therapist can engage the patient in making plans—even the simplest kind of plan, such as attending a lecture or concert next week, or keeping the next appointment, or accepting an invitation to a party two weeks from now—the patient is not committed to suicide. If the patient makes plans for the future spontaneously, the therapist can be reassured that the suicidal danger, for the moment at least, has somewhat lessened. The patient who has been considering the details of his suicidal plans in the office interview but terminates the interview by talking about the date he is going to have tomorrow afternoon is much less firmly committed to suicide than the patient who discusses the same kind of suicidal planning but who has no view to the future. The therapist must keep in mind the principle that the patient will perceive such planning as a demand, and it is therefore in the best interest of the patient that the planned activity be something that the patient can accomplish. Failure in attempting to carry out a plan that is too complex for the patient's level of functioning will compound the risk of suicide by reinforcing the patient's view of himself as worthless and as destined for future failures. On the other hand a planned activity can be a lifesaving measure when a chronic schizophrenic is contemplating in a nihilistic manner the meaninglessness of his existence.

An aspect of all three of the foregoing measures—interrupting isolation, enforcing activity, and making plans for the future—is included in the fourth therapeutic intervention, filling time. Time can be filled for the patient and with the patient through activities, through human contact, and through making plans. Filling time also has the important function of counteracting the feelings of emptiness so frequently seen in the schizophrenic patient. Some patients describe a kind of emptiness that aches and pains like a cavity in their chest. It is not the kind of empty feeling in the chest that is like the pleasant pain described by the lover who longs to be with his love; rather it is an empty, hollow, echoing hole that constantly craves filling, yet is never filled. This patient is like a barrel without a bottom into which love, affection, concern, and success can be poured but none of it stays. The process of filling time—occasionally even resorting to a highly compulsive filling of time—temporarily stills the pain of the emptiness and thus prevents suicide.

It becomes obvious that all of the foregoing techniques work temporarily and are designed to prevent the suicidal alternative to living while the patient plans a new way of relieving distress and of living more comfortably with his chronic illness. As the acute danger of suicide passes with the successful application of these temporary techniques, the therapist will find it useful to guide the patient in formulating a way of viewing his illness that will be stabilizing and that will help him to turn to living in the here and now with a less bleak view of his future. Just as many persons who suffer from chronic illnesses such as diabetes and heart disease can learn to manage their lives in such a way as to enjoy simple pleasures, so the person with a chronic mental illness can learn to manage his symptoms and to maximize his remaining adaptive functions. Thus, although he may realize that his illness persists, he will be less likely to react suicidally to the recognition that he continues to have the illness. Indeed, he will often reflect with a certain pride that he is managing his life so that few people in his world are aware of his illness.

During a period of active suicidal preoccupation it is

necessary with some patients to enforce controls—not the kind of control given by a hospital only, but also other external controls. For example, the therapist might be careful that all guns in the household are removed from the patient's access. He might insist with a patient who states his intention of buying a gun that if he does so hospitalization will then be necessary, and he will prohibit such an act. Most patients will tell the therapist such plans and thus will, in effect, ask for controls. The therapist might ask the patient to bring in all medications and take away from him all except those that he is currently using; he would not give him large prescriptions or renewable prescriptions that could possibly be used in a successful suicidal attempt. A chronically emotionally ill patient, in whom self-control is not so reliable as in the normal person, reacts to alcohol or drugs that alter his state of consciousness by becoming more poorly controlled. When suicide is a concern, it is more than ever important that the therapist arrange all possible controls to assist the patient in avoiding the use of alcohol or such drugs as barbiturates. All of these interventions are controlling, but also, of course, they demonstrate to the patient the therapist's concern and his wish to continue the relationship. When a chronically emotionally ill patient is also chronically suicidal and uses this threat frequently in his attempt to control the therapist, it is easy for the therapist to develop countertransference problems of such magnitude and so far removed from his awareness that he may be unconsciously helping the patient to commit suicide in order to alleviate the difficult situation. This danger must be carefully guarded against, and if any evidence of it occurs the therapist should obtain a consultation; he may even transfer the patient to another therapist.

We have already mentioned that many diverse people, agencies, and situations can be used to interrupt isolation. Another consequence of the patient's diffuse relationship to the world is that many of them can serve as agencies of the helping situation. Many patients need to be reassured constantly that help is available and that they are not alone. Such help can include the emergency hospital, the police department, the general hospital, the family physician, the psychiatrist, other therapists, Suicide Prevention Centers, churches, ministers, and many more. The very knowledge that there are services available twenty-four hours a day to which the patient can reach out frequently prevents suicide. We have known some patients who, when they become severely suicidal, call for the time on the telephone in order to hear a human voice. They know full well that it is a recording, but to them it represents a possible helping situation, an interruption of isolation, an activity, and a potentially therapeutic reminder that time continues and will continue.

All of these interventions are related to doing something with, or for, the patient. The final approach to suicide is to do something with the patient in terms of thinking about it. Certainly any hint of suicidal concern that the therapist detects in conversation with his patient should be explored and brought into the open. If the patient is thinking about suicide, he will surely not have the perspective on his possible death that the therapist will have. This approach includes the whole area of interpretive interventions. On occasion it is helpful with some patients to show them how the very thing that they fear the most, and that is central in their motivation for suicide, will surely come to pass if they do commit suicide. For example, the patient who is afraid of an interruption of his relationship to the therapist and who ruminates about being alone some day and being rejected can, on occasion, see the ridiculousness of suicide as an alternative when it is pointed out that the separation would then be final and irrevocable. On occasion the manipulative aspect of the suicide can be interpreted to the patient. It can be shown that this idea is being used by the patient in order to control the therapist and to get more of what he thinks he wants. It can be pointed out that the therapist does not want the patient to commit suicide. For some bright, thoughtful patients the

Hamlet conflict can be used in the interpretation. It can be pointed out that although the patient knows what he has now in terms of misery and suffering in the past and possibly in the future, he, of course, has no guarantees and knows nothing about what will happen after suicide and that whether he believes that he will sleep or be comfortable or be taken care of is an opinion based on faith and not on facts. Such discussions may interrupt the suicidal preoccupation long enough to allow the therapist to mobilize other resources and to change the picture markedly. It should also be pointed out to the patient that his suicide would have an effect on many people in his life, and that this effect is invariably one of making the lives of these people more troubled. The mobilization of guilt in the suicidal patient in this manner will frequently serve to remind him that he is not, in fact, so isolated as he has felt, because of the effect that his death would have on the lives of these people.

That suicide is a major problem in all societies and especially among patients with chronic emotional illnesses is obvious from a perusal of statistics. Today, in the United States, suicide is fourth in the leading causes of death. If more adequate systems of reporting suicide were available and if all of the suicides were considered—including medical suicides, that is to say, of patients who do not take care of their medical illnesses because they no longer wish to live—the rate of suicide would be even higher and might turn out to be the leading cause of death. It is a major problem and requires skilled and active intervention. One of the problems of the chronically emotionally ill patient, especially the chronic schizophrenic, is that frequently suicide is not clearly related to depression. In the depressed patient, chronic or acute, one is much more able to monitor the suicidal risk at any given moment by following the depression. In the chronic schizophrenic patient, depression is frequently absent or is only implied, and it is difficult to monitor the suicidal intent. One might see a patient in an office without noticing any evidence of depression and then discover that one hour later the patient has committed suicide without making elaborate plans or doing much thinking about the process. This kind of suicide is not preventable, yet the vast majority of suicides can be prevented temporarily by the methods outlined in this chapter. If suicide is temporarily prevented, then the techniques of developing the type of doctor-patient relationship advocated in this book can be employed. In such an emotional climate, at least suicidal intent will be more overtly communicated and at best the homeostasis of the patient's adjustment will be sufficiently altered that he no longer finds it necessary to consider suicide as an alternative to living.

14

The Family of the Patient

———————————————————◆
———————————————————◆
———————————————————◆

In the management of the patient with a chronic mental illness, the therapist must become involved with the family of which the patient is a member. The psychoanalytic model of psychotherapy concerns itself primarily with the internal family of the patient—that is to say, with the aspect of the family that the patient has symbolically internalized and with which he is struggling within himself. The real, objective family is not made a part of the treatment. With the patient with a chronic, severe emotional illness, such as schizophrenia, however, besides dealing with these internalized family members, the therapist must deal with the reality of the existing family. This is necessary because the patient requires help in managing his relationships with his family and because the family may provide a great deal of support and help in the task of increasing the patient's ability to function. If the family is not managed, it may interfere with the therapist's effort at providing support. Since the therapist is an important part of the patient's life over a long period of time, he must necessarily have contact with the existing family members.

In becoming involved with a new patient, the therapist must deal with all of the family's feelings about the patient's illness and about the intervention of a "stranger" (the therapist) in family matters. Usually by the time the patient seeks psychiatric help, the family has already become thoroughly imbued with the popular conception of pathogenesis in mental illness. Fathers and mothers feel guilty for the psychopathology of their children. Spouses are prepared to blame themselves for precipitating psychotic episodes in the other member of the marital union. Family members tend to deal with the discomfort caused by such guilt by looking for someone to blame; this someone may be the patient, a family member, a physical condition, or even the psychotherapist. It is therefore of the utmost importance for the psychotherapist to include in his treatment intervention with a new patient for whom he is prepared to provide supportive care by making some contact with other members of the family. This contact is of value in demonstrating that the therapist is concerned with the total situation in which the patient lives. It allows the family to see that this concern is realistic and includes an interest in the significant and important members of the patient's immediate reality. Early contact with the family prevents the major misinterpretations that occasionally result when the patient reports to the family certain statements by the therapist—frequently statements taken out of context. If a route of communication has not been opened at the very beginning of treatment, the family members may be reluctant to contact the therapist; they may assume that statements reported to them by the patient are indeed correct representations of the therapist's feelings and ideas. If the family's reaction toward such distorted statements is defensive and

hostile, individual family members may unnecessarily interfere with the treatment, undermine the therapist in the eyes
of the patient, and even encourage the patient to terminate
treatment. Obviously, such interruption of treatment and such
interference by the family cannot serve the patient's best
therapeutic interest, even if the patient himself participates in
such acting out. If early contact has been made with members of the family, however, and has provided them with the
possibility of communication throughout the long period of
treatment, they will more readily feel free to contact the
therapist to share with him their concern about the patient's
difficulties and behavior.

One of the tasks that must be dealt with during the beginning of supportive care is the definition and clarification of
the role of the therapist in the family situation. Is he an agent
of the patient, or is he an agent of the family? Does he hold
in confidence information told him by the patient as well as
by the family? The answers to such questions are not so clear
and simple as we might wish. Obviously, the therapist must
be firmly allied with the patient, and, in general, must function as an agent of the patient. In his role as therapist he
must keep information confidential, although he may, at times,
with the patient's permission, make reports to the family
about the psychotherapeutic process and about his concerns
with the patient. That does not mean that the therapist communicates to the family specific content of the therapeutic
transaction; rather he conveys general concerns and problems.
When a crisis arises in which the family must intervene, the
therapist should first approach the patient with the necessity
for communicating this information to the family. For example, if the therapist becomes increasingly concerned about the
patient's suicidal intent and if he feels that the family must be
informed in order to take steps to prevent suicide, the therapist must ask the patient's permission to communicate this
information to the family. If the patient refuses this permission, the therapist may then say to the patient that his

professional judgment dictates that he inform the family, even though the patient does not wish it. Usually patients will finally give consent for such communication if the therapist is firm in his expression of the need for involving the family. If the patient does not consent, the therapist may eventually contact the family without permission, but he invites the patient to be present at the time of this communication.

When family members communicate with the therapist and request that he not tell the patient about the communication, it is important to insist that the reporting family member tell the patient that he has called the therapist. If the family member refuses, the therapist must tell the patient, "Yesterday I received a call from X, who said that he was very much concerned about the fact that you are again spending a great deal of time in bed." In reporting such information to the patient, it is essential to convey the positive aspect of the family member's communication; that is to say, his concern for and his interest in the patient. In general it is best for the therapist to de-emphasize the negative aspects of the communication, such as accusations, complaints, and hopeless feelings.

The therapist's purpose in any intervention he makes with the family is to maximize its value in supporting the patient's functioning and to prevent disruptive, disorganizing influences as much as possible. Most of the patients who are in need of supportive care have families who show much behavioral pathology. The pathology and disorganization of the family may be etiologically relevant to the patient's behavioral disorganization, or it may be a reflection of a process in which marginal people tend to find one another and relate to one another. In spite of the great amount of pathology we see in the families of our patients, however, and in spite of the fact that we can often identify family behavior that results in major problems of disorganization for our patients, it is usually an error to take the position that removing a patient from his family will benefit him. Rarely will such a step be of assistance. More often it is correct to take the position that, no matter how "bad" the family appears to be, it is still the only and the best family the patient has. If the therapist encourages the patient to reject his family, he may also be encouraging him to give up an important actual or potential source of support. It is essential that the therapist be realistic about the family. At times he must help to restore the patient's perspective in regard to the disruptive influences of the family. It is often useful to remind the patient that his family can provide interest, concern, and rewarding, safe relationships if properly managed. It is not the task of the therapist to identify pathological trends in family members and to point these out to the patient while encouraging him to reject the family members. It is the task of the therapist to manage the total family situation with all of its pathology and disruptive influences. The purpose of such management is to provide an important source of support for the patient. Even a disorganized family, with proper management, is more therapeutic than a psychiatric hospital.

How can the therapist intervene specifically with the family to obtain support for the patient's functioning?

1. An obvious and important function of the therapist is to *give information* to the family. Often we see patients who have been in treatment for years with a number of psychiatrists, but where the family has received no information about the nature of the illness, the difficulties to be expected, the prognosis, and the kinds of situations in which they might be of help. We frequently see members of the family who are unable to give the support that they wish to give and that they could give if only a therapist had given them information and guidance. Some family members have an idea that they do not have a right to know about the patient's problems. They believe that their only function is to pay the bill for the psychotherapy. When we do see family members and give information, we can frequently mobilize a family to be highly supportive to the patient.

2. The therapist can be helpful in *relieving* the family of the amount and kind of *guilt* that interferes with their ability to be supportive to the patient. Parents in our society are ready to accept blame for their children's psychopathology and emotional problems; husbands and wives frequently see themselves as the cause of episodes of mental illness; and children readily accept guilt for "not doing enough" for their parents. Such guilt in the family brings about disorganization and malfunctioning in the patient. At times the guilt seems appropriate; but even if it is appropriate the therapist usually finds that the patient reacts maladaptively when the family is responding in terms of such guilt. Often, of course, the guilt is not appropriate, and the therapist must make special efforts to relieve the family members of it, not so much for their benefit as for the benefit of the patient. The family that feels guilty about the patient's illness tends to withdraw, to deny, to be punitive, and to fail to offer effective support. So much has been written in the lay literature about the schizophrenogenic mother and the "double-bind" theory of the etiology of pathological behavior that it is at times difficult to relieve a family of guilt. On the other hand, appropriately pointing out to members of the family that no one knows the cause of schizophrenia, that although there are many theories that relate the etiology of schizophrenia to the earliest human relationships there are also many theories that view the schizophrenic reaction as the result of impaired physiology and impaired genetics, may be enough to offer some relief of guilt to members of the family. To point out to them that after all they, too, are people and have their own needs and that they do the best they can under the circumstances is also an effective way of relieving some of the incapacitating guilt in the families of chronically ill patients.

3. The therapist can offer a great deal of *support* to the family of the patient so that they, in turn, can be supporting to the patient. For example, the therapist, by letting significant family members know that he can appreciate how diffi-

cult it is to live with the patient and to tolerate the patient's disorganized behavior, can be highly supportive. It is often necessary to remind the family that there are many times when the patient is relatively unencumbered by the symptoms of his illness, and that during these extensive periods he is a rewarding and gratifying member of the family. Especially when this step is combined with relieving guilt and giving information, many families are able to reorganize to such an extent that they can rally to the patient's support at moments of crisis.

4. After the therapist has had contact with the family of the patient, he can also serve the important function of *relieving them of some of their responsibilities*. If the therapist clearly identifies himself as responsible, as someone who is interested in the patient and in his family and who sees it as his job to maximize the patient's ability to function with a minimum amount of disorganization in the rest of the family, and if he portrays himself as a knowledgeable and skilled therapist, he may bring about a great deal of relief from responsibility for other members of the family. They may feel that now the patient and the whole problem are in the hands of a capable manager who can handle whatever needs to be handled and who is prepared for any emergency. Such a partial relief from responsibility by shifting the leadership of the supporting treatment team from a member of the family to the therapist can be useful in reorganizing the family for more effective support for the patient.

5. Even beyond these services to the family, the therapist should and can give actual *guidance* to them in their management of their supporting roles. He can specifically prescribe for members of the family the kind of thing that they can do to be helpful to the patient in offering support. Of course, in making such prescriptions it is essential that the therapist know the needs and limitations of the members of the supporting family, as well as knowing the needs and limitations of the patient. To make prescriptions of behavior for mem-

bers of the family that they cannot possibly fulfill will only produce more guilt and more disorganization, which will secondarily impair the patient's functioning.

Thus, in the management of the patient's illness, the therapist can be most effective in mobilizing a family for the support of the patient by *giving information, relieving guilt, sharing responsibility, offering support* to members of the family, and giving *guidance* in the management of the patient's behavior. Furthermore, the therapist can serve a useful function in *defining the roles* of the members of the supporting family. He may be able to do so primarily in his psychotherapeutic contact with the patient, or he may be able to do it through contacts with the entire family. Some therapists have found it useful to see the patient and the family together in order to focus on role definition with a view toward mobilizing support for the patient.

If the therapist begins to work with family members, he must be careful not to lose sight of the primary patient. Frequently he will see other members of the family who seem to have as much difficulty, disorganization, and pathology as the one who was originally referred for treatment and who is defined as "the patient." He may be tempted to define another member of the family as the patient; doing so, however, will be likely to result in severe disorganization of the primary patient's behavior. At times it may be necessary to "treat" other very sick members of the family by seeing them with the purpose of getting them to offer support to the primary patient, or it may be necessary to refer some members of the supportive family to another psychotherapist for treatment. If other members of the family are insistent that they too should be considered patients and should have the privilege of seeing the therapist for their problems, it is generally an indication that the therapist has not offered enough support and guidance to the members of the family. The others may want to become patients in order to compete for the therapist's concern and acceptance.

On occasion, a particular member of the family has such serious problems that it is necessary to refer him for psychotherapy. In general, a different psychotherapist should treat the other family member. Of course, when several therapists are involved it is necessary that they communicate with each other at frequent intervals, so as to minimize the confusion of having split direction for the supporting family. It is especially important that the therapists avoid competing with each other to see who can do the better job of getting his patient to outdo the other's patient in adequate functioning. Such competition inevitably becomes a model for competition among the members of the family. We have never seen a favorable outcome from such competition. For this reason we have often found it useful that the "psychotherapy" for the secondary patient be administered by a person who represents a different discipline; it may, for example, be the family's general physician, their minister, or a family service social worker.

There are special situations involving the family that we must consider in some detail here. The first of these is the problem of managing the family when the patient needs to be hospitalized. As we have mentioned in Chapter 7, in which we discussed the prescription for hospitalization, such a step frequently symbolizes to the patient the total failure of his adaptive capacity. Not only does this failure become reified to the patient, but it frequently becomes a problem to the family. They may individually or collectively feel that the need for hospitalization is the result of their failure to provide the kind of environment in which the patient could continue to exist. Such feeling of failure results in guilt, which then secondarily complicates the hospitalization for the patient. If the hospitalization is at all extensive, the family may deal with their anxiety, guilt, and hostility toward the patient by restructuring their interactions in such a way that the patient is permanently "organized out" of its structure. This danger is especially grave because it threatens to remove from the patient a potential source of support in the management of his illness at the time when hospitalization is no longer desirable. In general, we can prevent such restructuring by offering proper support to the family, as outlined above, and by keeping the family very much involved with the patient, with the therapy process, and with the therapist during the hospitalization. From the day the decision is made to have the patient hospitalized, the family must be involved in planning for discharge. With such an approach it never becomes possible for the family to think of itself as functioning without taking responsibility for the patient.

The second problem that must be dealt with in managing the family of the patient with chronic mental illness is the attitude of the family toward the chronicity of the patient's problem. Frequently an attitude of hopelessness and of diminished involvement characterizes the slowly declining effectiveness of the family in providing support. At times the family may directly demand from the therapist that he spell out in considerable detail the prognosis for the patient's future functioning. This question needs to be handled very much as it is handled with the patient. The point has to be made that the future will bring difficult times and will bring better times, and that with proper management and support, the complications of the patient's disorganized behavior can be minimized. In conveying this information to the family, it is of value to show how their support will participate in improving the patient's functioning and to point out that their support must be offered over long periods of time, perhaps indefinitely.

Many families have looked in the dictionary for definitions of schizophrenia and psychosis. They then believe that the course is necessarily and relentlessly downhill, that they have nothing to look forward to except more disorganized behavior on the patient's part and that ever-increasing support will be needed. It is with misconceptions such as these that the therapist can be most effective in altering the family's attitudes. He can give the family information that demon-

strates that the course of chronic mental illness is not relentlessly downhill; that, on the contrary, with proper management many patients who have such an illness function
remarkably well over long periods of time with a minimum of
support. Some of them may permanently go into such excellent social remission as to function indefinitely, using only in-
formally defined agencies of support. Such information can
give hope to the family and thus make it possible for them
to continue to function in their supporting roles over long
periods of time. Many families foresee no relief from their
functioning in the supporting role, and older parents are
concerned about the fate of their chronically mentally ill child
after the family no longer exists as an intact entity. Again, the
therapist can be of help by giving information that shows how
patients can learn to obtain support from agencies in our
society such as clubs, churches, fraternal organizations, and
marital partners. The family might even participate with the
psychotherapist in helping the patient to include such agencies as sources of support.

The therapist must be prepared to deal with the family
that comes to him with concerns and fears about the patient's
potential for homicide, suicide, destructiveness, and other aspects of abnormal behavior. When the supporting family has
such fears they are, of course, conveyed to the patient and can
have a disorganizing effect on him, especially since he too
shares the family's concern about his tenuous control of impulses. Perhaps the most effective way for the therapist to
deal with the family's fears and anxieties is to demonstrate
to the family his competence, his reliability, and his willingness to take responsibility. If he can assure the family that he
is considering their concerns seriously, yet that on the basis of
his professional knowledge he does not share their fears and
that he is willing to do whatever might be necessary in the
future to prevent the patient from becoming homicidal, suicidal, or destructive, the family can frequently find enough
reassurance to give up its fears. Fear of the patient's un-

manageable behavior is frequently a manifestation of the family's anxiety. This anxiety must be understood and can be handled in terms of the family's needs. With enough support, the family is usually willing to allow the therapist to take responsibility for worrying about aspects of the patient's behavior that might lead to homicide, suicide, or other destructive behavior.

On occasion, we see families who are capable of giving support to the patient but who also have a need to maintain the patient in the sick role. For these families the maintenance of the patient in the sick role preserves the stability of other members of the family. Paradoxical as it may seem, it is possible for a family to reinforce the patient's pathological disorganization and yet to offer support to the patient and to keep him functioning at a level that he could not maintain without such a family. The therapist who recognizes such a situation must tread very lightly in the intervention. He must consider all aspects of the homeostasis, constantly reminding himself that any change that permanently alters it may also make it impossible for the patient to obtain support. Once such a situation has been recognized, the approach and intervention must be based on a thorough knowledge of the patient and of each member of the family. Simply to point out the behavior of a family member—either to him or to the patient—is not of value. It is of value for the therapist to offer enough support to the various members of the family, either directly, by his own intervention, or by having a co-therapist provide such support, so that family members can give up behavior that maintains the patient in the sick role.

On rare occasions, the therapist may come to the conclusion that the patient should be removed from and isolated from the family. In the past, this type of intervention with the family has been much too readily utilized and has resulted in permanently losing support for the patient, who desperately needs such support. When all else fails, however, and when it is repeatedly demonstrated that the family is destructive to the patient's functioning, it may be necessary for the therapist to suggest isolation of the patient from the family. The therapist must recognize that this undertaking is necessarily risky. It means that the therapist has to provide even more support and may even have to participate in helping the patient to find substitute support. It means also that the therapist must be prepared to deal with the patient's guilt in giving up his own family. Withdrawal from the family may be too difficult for the patient to handle, especially when it expresses the negative aspect of his ambivalence toward the supporting situation. To advise a patient to interrupt his relationship with his family temporarily or permanently also requires the therapist to deal with the patient's reluctance to get himself involved with another supporting situation. A patient may avoid involving himself with another source of support because it might prove equally disappointing. It then becomes necessary to show the patient that the closeness of the members of the real family interferes with their attempt to be supporting, and that a relative stranger can do so more effectively. Even under such circumstances, when the therapist advises the patient's separation from the family, it is important to support the positive aspects of the patient's ambivalent feelings toward the family. If the therapist supports the negative aspects, he may by his action also be supporting the patient's negative transference toward the therapist, in which case the patient may find himself forced out of therapy and thus without any support, resulting in total disorganization of functioning.

In general, then, it is clear that any therapist who, over long periods of time, provides patients with supportive care for chronic mental illness must become involved with the families of his patients. It is his task to manage the family in such a way as to maximize its effectiveness in providing support for the patient and to minimize its disorganizing influence. The therapist can do so by intervening with the family in relieving their guilt, relieving them of responsibility, giving information, giving support, giving guidance, and defining roles within the structure of the supporting family unit.

15

Case
Histories

```
━━━━━━━━━━━━━━━━━━━━━━━━━━━━━━━━━━━━━━━━━━━━━━━━ ◆
━━━━━━━━━━━━━━━━━━━━━━━━━━━━━━━━━━━━━━━━━━━━━━━━━━ ◆
━━━━━━━━━━━━━━━━━━━━━━━━━━━━━━━━━━━━━━━━━━━━━━━ ◆
```

Ruth Ketch, a twenty-five-year-old, single, Jewish girl, came into treatment in the following manner. Her mother, who lives in Portland, Oregon, some 1,000 miles away from my office, read about some of my work in the local newspapers. These newspaper accounts stressed the short-term approach to treatment. She flew to Los Angeles and insisted on an appointment, wanting to know the details of our approach and asking whether her daughter would be eligible for our techniques. At this time, she was assured that her daughter's problems sounded quite different from those to which we addressed ourselves with brief treatment techniques and it was suggested that she continue her daughter under the care of a local psychiatrist. The mother left, only to reappear again several months later, stating that she was still dissatisfied with her daughter's treatment and that the diagnosis of chronic schizophrenia had been made. The daughter was not functioning well in any way. At this time she was living at home with her parents and a younger sister who was in college; she was not working, was not attending school (she had dropped out of the university in her third year with failing grades), and was spending most of her time in bed. Her parents were ashamed of her, not knowing what to say to their friends about her activities. The home situation was difficult for them and for her. When her mother came for the second time it was suggested that perhaps she should take her daughter to a good private hospital for treatment. After consultation with a hospital the patient was sent there and remained six months. She left the hospital because "I wasn't getting any help," and because her parents felt that she was not well handled. Essentially, the parents "rescued" her from the hospital when she called them one day and asked to be taken home because she did not like her doctor or the treatment she was receiving. After this six-month period of treatment the patient returned home and again was placed under the care of a local psychiatrist. Within a few months, once again, the parents were disenchanted with his approach to treatment and her mother flew to Los Angeles, most insistent that I should see the patient and take over her treatment. Again I assured her that I did not have time available, and after consultation with the treating psychiatrist I referred the patient to a competent psychotherapist in the Los Angeles area. The patient was sent to the psychiatrist, who agreed to treat her and placed her in a foster home with a social worker who was to supervise her activities. After approximately two weeks, the patient called her parents, requesting to be taken back home because she did not like the foster home. The patient was taken back to Portland, where she was placed under the care of a clinical psychologist who dealt with her in psychotherapy and encouraged her to find her own apartment. At this point, the parents became very much concerned about the consequences of the patient's poor judgment, about her inability to handle money, about her inability to manage relationships, and about a number of inappropriate sexual involvements with men. Generally, their attitude toward their daughter was characterized by shame and guilt and suppressive measures. At this point, they once again contacted me and prevailed on me to see the daughter.

As I examined this patient she appeared to be a very immature, loud-talking, twenty-five-year-old woman whose childish and obsequious behavior quickly became difficult to bear. She related with much frankness all of the details of her history, talking in great detail about the many difficulties she had with her parents. She displayed a remarkable naïveté in regard to human relationships and related that her most recent affair with a much older man had started when "I felt sorry for him" because he had not had sexual relations for several weeks. She described how she felt herself responsible for the whole family, stating that her mother was very unhappy, that her father was very unhappy, and that her sister was not performing her duties at home. Apparently, she was eager to begin treatment and explained, "I will do anything that is asked of me." On psychological examination she demonstrated poor grasp of reality, marked loosening of associations, inappropriate affect, and an immobilizing ambivalence. At the same time, I interviewed both parents and found the father to be an elderly, retired, henpecked, duty-bound piano salesman, who had been suffering all of his married life from the results of an unfortunate choice of mate. His wife, who every other minute reminded everyone present that she used to be a nurse and that she had given up her career in order to marry, was an overbearing, loud, controlling, complaining, correcting Jewish mother, in the worst sense of the term. She had a way of making everyone around her feel guilty and constantly reminded all who would listen of her martyrdom. She was obviously a very unhappy person who produced a great deal of misery in everyone around her. She stated that she was so distraught over her daughter's illness that she saw no reason for going on living; all she wanted her daughter to do was to get well so that she, the mother, would have reason to live again. She also stated that perhaps it would be best to kill herself and her daughter, and then everyone would be better off. At this remark, her husband looked with sad, pleading eyes at his wife, imploring her not to commit suicide or murder, and then looked toward me as if to say, "You see, the poor woman suffers so much that we must do something." Through all of this, the patient demonstrated a great deal of manipulative ability, constantly playing the game of "Let's you and him fight." When I attempted, in the first interview, to confront the family with their dynamics, they all looked at me with wide-eyed innocence, as though I were a nasty-minded man with evil thoughts.

After very carefully considering this difficult situation, I felt that I could be of assistance to this family, if they were willing to let me take over and to accept my directions. Since they came from several hundred miles away, I was readily accepted as an authority figure, as is frequently the case. The farther the patient travels to the consultant, the wiser and more prominent the consultant appears to be. I agreed to take on the treatment of Ruth, explaining that there would be a two-month wait while I made arrangements for her care in Los Angeles. I explained to the parents that the patient would move to Los Angeles, would be placed in a living situation that I would find, and would be placed in an activity therapy program that I would devise. The parents' part would be not to communicate with her or interfere with the treatment. They would have contact with the patient only through me. I told them that only under these circumstances would I take on the treatment and that if there were any interference from them, it would be terminated immediately. I had decided before this interview that if I accepted this patient for treatment, I would have to insist on absolute control. The history of this case demonstrated that all treatment had failed because the family had constantly interfered and the patient had manipulated the therapists. Since I represented a last resort to them, they apparently were willing to accept this control, and the patient arrived with six suitcases one Monday morning to begin treatment.

During the two months' preparation I had made arrangements at a local residence for adult single people for the patient's board and care. I had been informed by the parents that the patient had never written checks and did not know how to manage money. I therefore set a monthly allowance of $250 from which the patient was expected to pay all of her expenses except therapy. I also made contact with an occupational therapist who was to see the patient for guidance in living and activity therapy four times a week, whereas I would see the patient once a week. The patient arrived at the activity therapist's studio with the six suitcases mentioned previously. As a first step, five of these suitcases were sent back home with the parents, and the patient, with one suitcase, was transported by the activity therapist to the boarding house. The parents were not allowed to see this home, since they would, no doubt, have remarked that it was not luxurious or pleasant enough. The parents were told not to contact the patient by telephone, not to come to visit her, and to write once a week only, unless otherwise directed by the therapist. They were encouraged to call the therapist at any time to communicate any of their worries. They were instructed that if they were called by the patient in regard to any matter whatever, they were to call the therapist immediately. The patient knew about these instructions to the parents. They were also told that if the patient called them and said that she was going to commit suicide unless they came at once (which was how she had manipulated them in the past), they should encourage her to call me, and at the same time the parents should alert me to the situation.

Treatment for the patient began with a firm insistence on a carefully laid out and structured plan of activity. The patient was to learn in the first few weeks how to write checks, how to pay her bills, and how to get about town on a bus. She was to involve herself with various appropriate activity and youth groups in the Los Angeles area. In order to carry out these goals, she saw me once a week. We focused our discussion on her relationships to people during the week with an emphasis on reality, on the here and now, and on activity. I insisted that she must expose herself to human relationships every day, no matter how difficult it was for her. Four times a week the patient went to the activity therapist, where she began by learning such simple tasks as washing her clothes (which she had never done, since at home everything was done for her), writing checks, adding and subtracting, learning how to manage her money, and preparing herself for future employment. The patient was maintained on mild anti-anxiety medication—chlordiazepoxide (Librium) 25 mg. t.i.d. Her "terrible menstrual cramps," which her mother had described as requiring that she go to bed for three days each month with large dosages of codeine, were handled by placing her on norethindrone (Ortho-Novum), 2 mg. daily, twenty days a month. This measure had the secondary benefit of preventing pregnancy in case she exposed herself to this possibility. She was also encouraged during the initial weeks of treatment to call the therapist whenever she felt upset. She was told that she would be expected to keep her therapy appointments no matter what. She was also encouraged to come by bus, rather than to have someone drive her to her appointments. During the first few weeks she found it difficult to manage her anxiety. She became involved in a number of relationships with people, relationships that frequently ended in rejection. During this period she had two very brief, impulsive sexual affairs, each on a first date. Each of these incidents was used to demonstrate to her the inappropriateness of her judgment. At no time was she told that she should not become sexually involved. Rather the point was made that she should become sexually involved only if she wanted to, not simply to please someone else or because she did not know what else to do. The constant stress in the psychotherapeutic interviews was on her taking responsibility for her own behavior and actions. As she became frightened, as she talked about not being able to manage, as she felt like flying home, firm structure was imposed. She was assured that the therapist was concerned, and she was told that her anxiety was to be expected. She was reminded that she had agreed to undertake this treatment no matter how difficult and how painful it would be. She was rewarded with praise for not running home, for not involving her parents, and for not checking out of treatment. A number of crises occurred with the parents. After approximately three days, they called to find out how the girl was doing, since she had not "written yet." I pointed out to them that I had taken responsibility for asking her not to write to them more than once a week. I suggested that she had some right to privacy and that they should not expect to know all the details of her everyday life. Privacy had been a problem in the home and, in fact, the mother had pried by listening to telephone conversations and by steaming open letters that the patient received from friends. The parents accepted authoritative direction from me on how they should write, how much money they should send, and how they should talk to their daughter. The first telephone call by the daughter to the parents was made in my office in my presence. When she became so emotional that she could not continue talking, I took the telephone and explained to the parents that she was upset by the conversation but that otherwise she was doing fine. At this point, the patient was able to take over and to continue the conversation with her parents.

During the following months, the patient re-enacted the home situation with the psychotherapist and the activity therapist. She would play one off against the other; she would tell each one that he was wonderful and that she did not get much from the other; and she would report back and forth what one or the other had said, distorting it in the direction of her own agenda. It was only through constant, almost daily communication between the activity therapist and the psychotherapist that the acting out could be prevented. The patient was constantly confronted with the fact that the therapists were communicating with each other, that they had no secrets from each other, that they would not engage in any conspiracy against each other, and that both of them were working for the one goal of helping the patient to become independent, to grow up, and to live the kind of life that she wanted to live after she had defined that life. After approximately eight months of guided existence in the boarding home, with increasing emphasis on her participation in groups, the patient became socially more outgoing. At this point a situation was found for her in a sheltered workshop. Here she was able to do minor production work under supervision, something she had never been able to do. All of her life she had worked in her father's music store without pay and without any kind of adequate work expectations. During the few months before beginning treatment, she had attempted a number of jobs, including being a cashier in a cafeteria, but she had failed at it after one or two days because she could not handle her anxiety. She was placed in a sheltered workshop where the employers were aware of her anxiety problems and where she could work half a day at limited pay under supervision. In this experience she gained some confidence in her ability to function and was very proud of her first few pay checks, the first she had ever received in her life. Her parents attempted on several occasions to interfere, calling me to state that Ruth was always telling them that she did not like office work and that they did not think she ought to get started in office work. They wanted her to do volunteer work in a hospital, a setting that I felt was strongly contraindicated and that I would not permit. There were many occasions when Ruth did not write her parents. Each time a letter was missed, the parents would call me frantically, wondering what was going on. I always reassured them, telling them that Ruth was doing well. Then I would encourage Ruth to write a letter, because after all her parents seemed to need some reassurance that things were going satisfactorily for her. She could accept this reason for writing and usually complied with my request.

It is thus far that treatment has progressed. Essentially,

it has consisted of offering to a chronic schizophrenic patient a consistent relationship, guiding her life situation, providing structure, and emphasizing activity. The patient was able to move rapidly in the direction of growth and integration to the extent that she now has almost become an independent human being. She will in the future enter more complex relationships, such as marriage. These relationships will pose many threats, which will need to be worked out with the therapist and which will need to be evaluated and supervised over many years to come. Many of Ruth's new friends do not know how sick she is and in fact at times support her in her attempt to leave therapy. When she functions well, her severe schizophrenic impairment is not obvious. Her parents have withdrawn some- what from Ruth and are now attempting to re-create the situation with her younger sister. Her ego strength is con- siderably greater than Ruth's, however, so that she is able to make plans for leaving home and going to college far away. Apparently she is not schizophrenic.

I first met Michele Vickers when she was eighteen and just out of high school and I was a young and relatively in- experienced therapist—certainly one unwise in the ways of supportive care. I was on the staff of a mental hygiene clinic attached to a psychiatric hospital, and Michele was brought to my office one afternoon after having nearly been hit by a car. She had explained to the driver, who had stopped to render assistance, that she had been following a beckoning vision of Jesus that had appeared to her in the street and that she had not noticed his car. She accompanied this Sa- maritan unquestioningly and unprotestingly to the clinic, where it quickly became apparent to me that, although she had suffered an acute hallucinatory experience, it was not a toxic reaction. She exhibited all of the classical manifestations of schizophrenic reaction, including autism, associational disturbance, ambivalence, and affective disturbance. I recom- mended to her that she undertake weekly outpatient treatment in our clinic, to which she agreed, but since she was a minor it was necessary to obtain her parents' consent. To my surprise I discovered that her father and stepmother were totally unwilling to accept the fact that she was ill and in need of treatment. After considerable pressure on my part, they reluctantly consented to her keeping on with the out-patient visits, but after four or five visits it was apparent that her illness was becoming more severe and more disruptive of her level of functioning. Looking back at these outpatient visits from the perspective of my present experience, it seems likely that I was contributing to the increasing severity of her symptoms, because I was spending much of my time with her in doing the kind of detailed work-up or meticulous history for which I had been praised as a student. I am sure that we spent very little time in discussing the adequacy of her reality contact or the way in which she was increasingly failing to meet her responsibilities in her day-to-day existence. In any event, a period of grossly psychotic and bizarre behavior, which involved disrobing and acting out sexual fantasies with Jesus, made me and other clinic personnel decide that it was inappropriate to attempt to maintain her in the community. Thereupon the same sort of struggle with the parents over obtaining their consent occurred again, except that this time they were wholly unwilling to cooperate by giving their consent to her hospitalization. Unable to find any other responsible relatives who could help me to gain her parents' consent, I petitioned the Superior Court that Michele be committed to our hospital for treatment, which the court consented to do. It is still not clear to me after these years what specifically I failed to do to find a successful approach to these reluctant parents, but I am fairly sure that something in my manner of dealing with this problem was inappropriate, for I have never had such a situation recur.

The errors that I committed in dealing with this patient in an outpatient setting were compounded when I secured her admission to a locked ward for severely psychotic women.

The hospital was a rather old-fashioned, government-sponsored mental hospital, where it was assumed that any serious psychiatric illness would require months or years of hospitalization. I had not yet become aware of the dangers of prolonged hospitalization for chronically ill mental patients, and for many months I did nothing to cut through the hospital's red tape to secure her release. The situation was difficult at best, the family had been totally alienated from her by the way in which I had secured her hospitalization and were intransigent in their unwillingness to provide an extramural setting in which the patient's treatment could continue. After thirteen long months (which the patient and I continue to deplore to this day) I secured her placement in a foster home which, although it left much to be desired in the way of a structured milieu, did succeed in breaking the vicious circle in which the patient's existence had begun to move. Part of the environment in the foster home was to encourage patients to become self-supporting, and in my zeal to achieve therapeutic "success" I supported the emphasis on job seeking, thereby—I now realize—placing a demand on my patient with which she was unable to comply. She did obtain a job as a salesgirl and, within the first few days of her employment, met a young man with whom she accepted a date to go to a drive-in movie. While on this date she had her first complete sexual experience, and as a result of this experience she became pregnant. It was during her pregnancy that I began to practice some of the techniques of supportive care that now seem so rational to me because I know they are effective. I began to help her to structure her daily existence, I was careful not to encourage or insist on things that I thought she might not be able to achieve, and I was assisted in formulating this approach by her very wise and experienced obstetrician, who was staff physician to a home for unwed mothers. He, of course, had carried many a chronically schizophrenic young woman through an unplanned pregnancy and, although he had no theoretical formulation for his method of treatment, had a great deal to teach in the way of practicing successful supportive care.

I cannot relate here the details of the history of Michele's treatment since that time, for ten years have elapsed and much has happened. Briefly, her illegitimate child was placed for adoption, and she moved from the home for unwed mothers to a foster family in which there was maximal cooperation with the supportive program that I outlined. She met and subsequently married a teacher of accounting in a high school (who knew of her past illness and of her pregnancy), and she is now providing successful mothering to the two children who have been born to this marriage. For several years she and her family have lived in another city, and throughout this period she and I have given recognition to the fact that her continued good functioning is enhanced by her regular telephone chats with me on the fifteenth of each month. She has come to recognize that she has a chronic illness that is manageable as long as she continues to work at managing it. Her motivation to supply this effort is provided by her clear memory and vigilance regarding behavioral signs that the illness is still present somewhere underneath her successful façade. She can take pride and pleasure in recounting to me how a symptom has appeared in such attenuated form that it is not noticed by anyone except herself and in recounting to me the behavioral details of involving herself in organized and structured activity to combat the disorganizing effects of the symptom. She is grateful for the meaning that our relationship has added to her life. She is proud that her economic circumstances have now improved sufficiently to enable her to pay me a fee for our monthly telephone consultation, and on annual visits to her home town she takes pride in bringing her children to display to me and to express how she, as well as they, have grown. Her husband too, who is a highly organized and structured man, has taken well to his role of supplying a rather firm control and a high degree of organization, geared to those times when she feels that her own controls are relatively weak. He shares with me the pleasure of seeing her really excellent functioning in her roles as housewife and mother, in part because he is aware of the successful struggle that this behavior represents. She, like other patients we have mentioned, carries a few of the prescribed pills in a rather tattered container bearing the label of the pharmacy of the hospital in which she spent her thirteen, in many respects, wasted months. In a rather pointed way she tells me that this label reminds her of how important it is for her to stay well and yet how comforting it is to know that a haven exists for people who are ill, as she was and, indeed, as she might again become should her efforts at control fail.

I first met Reah Prepin, a forty-five-year-old stockbroker, in 1957 when she was hospitalized at a California state hospital. At that time she had recently been divorced, had made a suicidal attempt, and demonstrated all of the signs of schizophrenia, including marked loosening of association, autistic withdrawal, immobilizing ambivalence, and inappropriate affect. She had been picked up by the police for attempting to sell fictitious securities. At the time of her admission she thought she was Mother Mary. She remained in the hospital for approximately two months, after which she was discharged to aftercare.

I did not see her again for many years, although once a year I heard from her on a Christmas card. She continued to be quite successful in her stock transactions and accumulated considerable sums of money. Each time that she was several thousand dollars ahead, she would take a trip to the Orient or to Europe. She would disappear for three or four months, frequently in search of a "magic cure" for her bouts of depression. She must have visited most of the "quick magic doctors" on four continents, subjecting herself to all kinds of treatment, including injections of a "secret formula," bizarre surgery, special diets, and so forth. Each time she would respond dramatically, would gain new hope, and would feel that this latest treatment was the cure. Each time, however, after several months of treatment the same symptoms and hopelessness would reappear and again she would feel that nothing had been done for her. She did not seek psychotherapy because she was convinced of the organic etiology of her illness.

Approximately two years after her first hospitalization at the state hospital, she again become grossly bizarre, physically attacked a client, and was hospitalized at another state hospital. This time she stayed in the hospital approximately one year and had some eighty electroconvulsive treatments. She made no improvement and looked like the typical back-ward patient until one day a new doctor walked into the ward, "rescued" her, and took an interest in her. She then went into almost complete remission within a matter of weeks; she left the hospital and remarried. During subsequent years she continued to go from doctor to doctor, having the same experience each time. At first, the physician was of much help and his medicine was a special kind of magic, but after a few months the magic wore off. She exposed herself to many medications and, in fact, on occasion had rather serious physical complications, including liver and kidney problems resulting from the medication. She has taken almost every kind of psychopharmacological agent known. I had no contact with this patient for many years until suddenly, in November of 1964, she appeared in my private office stating that she needed an appointment. She stated that she had gained many pounds, that she was having many difficulties, that she was unable to function and unable to carry on in her job as a securities broker, and that she was at the end of her rope. She remembered that many years before I had been in favor of psychotherapeutic intervention, but she did not believe in psychotherapy then and still did not believe in it. Now she had tried all drugs and had run out of all possible resources, and she was willing as a "last resort" to try me. She also related that she had tried hypnosis and hypnotherapy and starvation diet during the last two years, none of which had helped.

On my examination, she demonstrated again all aspects of schizophrenia. She was delusional, having both delusions of grandeur and paranoid delusions; she showed marked loosening of associations; and she was angry at all doctors. She told me that she was trying me as a therapist, but that she did not really think I could be of help. I reviewed the situation in detail and decided to attempt treatment with techniques of supportive care. I met with her and her husband and outlined the treatment program, which consisted essentially of the following activities. She would see me once a week; she would have to force herself to stop spending all day in bed; she would not be allowed to go to bed until 9:00 in the evening and had to be out of bed each day at 8:00 A.M. Furthermore, she was required to go out of the house at least three times a day, if for nothing more than to go to the grocery store; she was expected to make three telephone calls a day; and I expected her to work in a broker's office rather than by herself. All of these regulations were made to insure some human contact each day other than with her husband. She had been spending the last few months mostly in bed, isolated from the world and hallucinating. She was asked to keep a log book, each day recording at least once an hour what was going on, how she was feeling, and what she was doing. This technique was used because in the past obsessive-compulsive defenses had served her well in warding off psychotic symptoms. Also, I told her that she should be available at the telephone each day at 6:00 P.M., when I would call her to see how she was doing and to give her further instructions.

During the subsequent four weeks we followed this program of treatment. Each evening, including Saturdays and Sundays, I called her, asked her what she was doing, and was firm and somewhat demanding in my attitude, giving her praise for following orders and suggesting that she could do better. I discussed with her each evening what she would serve her husband for dinner, and when she complained that she was too tired to do anything, I told her that she must force herself, no matter how she felt, to make dinner for herself and for her husband. Frequently she would become angry at me on the telephone, and during the weekly psychotherapy sessions she spent most of the time complaining about the demands I was making on her. She told me that I was a terrible doctor, how well she had been treated by the other physicians, and how much better she had been years ago. She also complained about feeling hopeless about ever improving and stated that she could do very little to help herself and that this was the end of the road. On several occasions during the next few months, she would spend the psychotherapy hour stating essentially, "I don't see any reason why I shouldn't kill myself. I'd probably be better off and certainly everyone else would be better off." I took the position with her that certainly I could not prevent her from committing suicide, but that I did not want her to commit suicide. I also stated to her that there were lots of other things to do besides committing suicide and that she had made a contract with me to work in therapy for some time in order to get help. Slowly, as the months went by, she improved in her functioning. She lost some weight, began to be more active in the selling of securities, and finally began to make some business deals. At first selling was difficult for her because she experienced each "no sale" as a personal rejection. At this time she would tell me on the telephone each day that in former times she had been enthusiastic and could get people to buy and sell, but that now they picked up her negativism and she could do very little. In spite of her negativism she began to sell. As these examples of her mild successes became apparent to her, she improved remarkably. During the next few months she continued to function better. The daily telephone calls were cut down to one a week between appointments. I placed her on a mild antianxiety drug to help her to handle her feelings more appropriately. As the depression began to lift, her schizophrenic symptoms showed remission. She apparently is receiving enough support from once-a-week appointments at this time to give up the extra telephone contact with me. She frequently still remarks that she is not as well as she used to be and that perhaps she has brain damage that makes it impossible for her to concentrate or to think as clearly as she has in the past. Each time that she brings up this material she is reminded of the fact that she has a long way to go and that we have much to work out for her. She is reminded to remain active, to expose herself to human contacts, and to function as much as she can on the job. Generally, my attitude has continued to be a kind but firm and somewhat demanding one. When she talks about the other physicians, now stating that they did not help her, I am very careful to avoid any stated or implied criticisms. I avoid criticisms of her previous doctors, even though I feel that their treatment was of no help, because in latent language she is talking about me when she discusses her previous therapists. If I were to hint at agreement, I would convey to her that I thought I could not be very helpful, a suggestion that would have disastrous results for the patient.

As she has improved, she has become increasingly concerned about other people. She is now worried about her husband and her mother, feeling that perhaps she has responsibility for their unhappy lives. I handle this material by stating that no doubt they were influenced by the problems of her illness, but that she cannot hold herself responsible. I remind her that she has been terribly ill, that she is still quite ill, and that perhaps she is expecting too much of herself when she thinks that she is responsible for the health and mental equilibrium of her husband and mother. These are the topics of her psychotherapy at this time.

I may say that during the past year and a half of treatment she has stabilized considerably, is able to function quite well, and lives a much less bizarre life. Symptoms have remained relatively in remission, although she continues to have periods of depression and feelings of hopelessness. The treatment has consisted primarily of providing a firm structure, of focusing on activities, of getting her off the hook of her guilt, and of offering her a consistent, morally nonjudgmental relationship. I make it quite clear that I have certain expectations of her. However, I spell out these expectations clearly by use of the position of authority which I as a physician hold in relation to this patient.

Richard Vernon is a twenty-six-year-old, single, graduate engineer who first consulted me in October 1957. Just before coming to see me, he had been a student at Boston University, taking his degree in engineering. During his last year of school he had been treated by a psychologist in Boston.

At the time that he came to see me, he reported his background as follows: he was the elder of two children of a father and mother who had worked in the garment industry all of their lives, and who lived with the mother's parents in the same house. His complaint consisted of being totally incapacitated at work for the past three months because he felt a constant urge to tear paper. He also had a facial tic and a compulsion to break pencils. He spent most of his time in obsessive rumination about tearing paper and breaking pencils. He had developed some auditory hallucinations consisting of voices threatening him with annihilation. He frequently had the urge to buy himself a gun to kill these voices or to kill himself. He further stated that he was "not a man" because he had never slept with a girl. He complained of emptiness and hopelessness and knew of no way to fill his time. He stated that he was able to function marginally at work as an engineer only because no one paid any attention to him and that they accepted his bizarre behavior because he had the reputation of being a genius. As soon as he finished work he would go to his modernistic apartment and lock himself in; there he would spend all of his time by himself, afraid of being with other people and with many preoccupations about his body. He was concerned with a receding hairline, with the size of his penis, and with various aches and pains in his body. He had noticed some "bugs" in the apartment and thought that the landlord had placed them there to scare him. At the time that he first came to me, he found it impossible to go to work during the day and had received permission from his employer to work at night. He would spend eight hours during the night sitting in his cubicle in front of the computer, trying to deal with the problems at hand but totally unable to function. He would spend much time ruminating about his social incapacities, about his lack of sexual involvement, and about what he felt was the small size of his sexual organ. He was very much afraid of losing control of his angry feelings toward everyone, and he had many fantasies about taking a machine gun to shoot his neighbors, to shoot his fellow engineers, or to shoot me. He went so far as to find out that he could not purchase a machine gun without a special license. He frequently woke up at night with nightmares, screaming, and with a feeling that his mother was poisoning him. He would then have vivid fantasies of killing his parents and grandparents, and when morning came he would call me to make certain that he really had not done so. He managed anxiety by drinking alcoholic beverages, mostly beer, until he calmed himself enough to sit in a stupor by himself. He had many fantasies about suicide, imagining how people would react if he disemboweled himself, hanged himself in a public place, and so on.

I considered hospitalizing him, but since he had had three previous hospitalizations of several months that had not helped in any way and that in fact had led to further incapacity each time, I attempted outpatient treatment. Treatment with this patient was undertaken in a highly structured context. He was told that he would be seen once a week. He was told that he was expected to work regular hours during the day, or at least to go through the motions of working. He was told to make some attempt to place himself in juxtaposition to other people each day, no matter how difficult it was for him. He was asked to participate in one group per week, using a directory of community activities as a guide to finding such groups. As a part of his project of living he was to write a report about each of these activities. He was also told to stop drinking alcoholic beverages (one twelve-ounce bottle of beer a day was permitted) and instead to use trifluoperazine (Stelazine), 5 mg., b.i.d., to deal with his anxiety. After approximately two months of treatment I received a letter from his family in Boston stating that they had received a letter from the patient telling them that he was going to commit suicide. I discussed the patient's serious illness with the family, who thought that perhaps he should again be hospitalized. After careful consideration of all of the risks involved I decided not to hospitalize him, since it would further alienate him from the real world and would encourage his accepting a helpless, hopeless role rather than utilizing his remaining adaptive capacities for functioning in life. I was able to reassure the parents during subsequent weeks by frequent telephone calls. Also I discussed with the patient his frequent aggressive suicidal threats. It became clear that his motivation for suicide was primarily as an aggressive act against his parents and me. In therapy together the patient and I considered the possibility of his expressing his aggressive, angry feelings in some more appropriate way that also would be less destructive to himself.

During the following year the patient stabilized considerably. On one of my trips to the East I visited with his parents, who came to see me at the airport, and discussed the whole situation with them. They seemed reassured by my interest in their son and were quite aware of the danger of suicide that was omnipresent. They suggested the possibility of his moving back to Boston, but in subsequent discussions both the patient and I resisted their suggestion, since he had never been able to function adequately in the home situation.

As treatment continued, the patient began reaching out

to other people. He was constantly afraid of rejection and usually, indeed, encountered rejection. These rejections were always caused by the patient's inappropriate behavior. For example, he made inappropriate, clumsy approaches to some girls living in his apartment house and was rebuffed. Actually, the patient was a very good-looking young man who had considerable financial means. He planned to approach girls for dates and wanted to say to them, "Will you go out with me?" At the same time he was thinking that perhaps if he dated a girl several times, he might be able to go to bed with her, since one of his major concerns was the fact that at age twenty-six he had never had sexual relations. He was especially tortured by the young engineers at work, who were constantly discussing the girls that they had enjoyed in bed. As a result of his anxiety and the disorder of his thought processes, he would find himself walking up to a girl who was sitting by the swimming pool of the apartment house in which he lived and saying, "Would you like to fuck with me?" He and the girl would both be horrified by the clumsiness of his approach.

In therapy with him in regard to this matter I took an attitude that conveyed that he was still quite young, that there was much time for him to enjoy sexual relations, and that perhaps it was too early for him, in view of his long-term and disabling illness, to become intimately involved. He would argue with me over this point. He would state that I had no understanding; that I did not know how painful it was for him not to have anyone. He would bring me all kinds of evidence to demonstrate his sexual deprivation as the primary problem. For example, one night with the computer, using medical and population statistics, he figured out that there were 24,600 kilometers of unused vagina in the United States each evening and that apparently he was unable to find the six inches that he required. Finally, he did find a colleague at work with whom he went to a Mexican border town, where he engaged the services of a prostitute. He was shocked by the event, thought she was a little girl, and felt extremely sorry for her. When he attempted coitus he began to vomit and ran away from the situation. A week later he appeared in my office horrified by the whole experience and furthermore complaining of a burning in his penis and a white discharge, which I diagnosed as gonorrhea after appropriate laboratory examination. I treated his gonorrhea. He concluded that sex was not what it was "cracked up to be" and that he could get along without it.

Treatment continued for approximately three years. During the time of his treatment with me he was able to continue functioning and in fact made some important creative contributions at work in developing a new concept for guidance systems. He continued to spend each therapy hour complaining about a multitude of physical symptoms, about his feelings of hopelessness, and about his suicidal thoughts because of his miserable existence. Yet, in spite of everything, he functioned better than he ever had when he was in a situation in which he felt demands were placed upon him. After two years of treatment he developed a rather formal relationship with a girl, his first girl friend. He took several trips East to visit his parents, but each time he would return quickly, not staying out the full two weeks of his vacation because he found himself totally unable to function at home.

After three years of treatment, suddenly the patient's grandmother died. At this time he came into a sum of money and his parents requested that he return to Boston. He himself felt that he would like to return to Boston to complete work on his Ph.D. I took the position that he should not do so, but that he should remain in California. The patient was unable to resist the offer of money and "comfort" at home, however, hoping that at home he could finish his year of school to complete his doctorate. The patient was reminded of the fact that he had had much difficulty at home previously and that perhaps this was not the time for him to leave California. Despite this strong stand by me, however, he did decide to

move back to Boston. He was referred to a competent therapist in that area.

In a matter of weeks in Boston his functioning declined.
He was unable to function sufficiently to apply to graduate
school, he spent all of his time at home, and in spite of excellent supportive care by the new therapist, he demonstrated an
exacerbation of symptoms. He continued to talk about suicide,
which resulted in hospitalization at the parents' insistence. He
remained in the psychiatric hospital for six months, showing constant regression of functioning, and eventually was
released when funds ran out. He stayed at home, did not
work, and lived a totally withdrawn existence. He was again
hospitalized, this time for a period of one year, and upon his
release from the hospital was again totally unable to function.
At this point he wrote me a letter stating that he would like
to come back to California to try to pick up the pieces of his
life. He wanted to get involved in therapy with me and to
attempt to return to his previous level of excellent functioning
that he had enjoyed in the West. I replied that I would be
happy to see him but that I thought he ought to discuss this
matter in detail with his present therapist. Since returning to
Boston his parents had changed his therapist six times. He did
discuss this matter with the current therapist, who advised
against the move to California. At this point the patient showed
further exacerbations of symptoms, including the demonstra-
tion of very poor impulse control when he struck his father
during an argument. He was again hospitalized in a private
psychiatric hospital where he remained a number of months.
Subsequently he was committed to a state hospital. At the
present time, several years later, he is still a resident of a
state hospital, existing on a chronic ward, totally withdrawn,
disheveled looking, unable to function even in the simple tasks
of the hospital routine. He has received a series of electroconvulsive treatments, to which he has not responded, and he is
now being maintained on large doses of phenothiazines. He
has become very fat and shows signs of "mental deteriora-

tion" in that he no longer appears to make use of his excellent intelligence. His parents visit him approximately once a month, but he responds very little to their visits. He has decided that he will remain in the hospital for the rest of his life, a decision that apparently is not disturbed by the hospital's program.

I think that the very unfortunate outcome of this case can be attributed to the incorrect use of the hospital. A therapist frequently finds himself in the position of having to take some risks with a patient, especially a patient like Richard Vernon who talks a great deal about suicide. Many therapists tend automatically to hospitalize a patient who talks about suicide. In fact, usually this is a method of temporizing with the suicidal problem and of doing what is "safest" for the therapist. As we have mentioned in our chapters on theory and technique, we must also consider the very real dangers of hospitalizing a patient. An incorrect decision to hospitalize will not demonstrate its dire consequences as immediately as a suicide would. In this case, certainly, the decision to hospitalize the patient heralded a disastrous turn of events. He has now become a chronic hospital cripple, unable to use his remaining adaptive capacities for the tasks of life. Had he not been hospitalized, perhaps he might have made a suicidal attempt, although a long history of suicidal ruminations showed no evidence that he had carried any of them into action. Furthermore, his capacity to reach out for people and to use a relationship with a therapist apparently had prevented him from becoming so desperate that he had to express his fate by suicide.

This patient's problems are now compounded and complex. Not only does he have all of the difficulties that result from his basic schizophrenic illness and that were present before hospitalization, but superimposed on them is the secondary invalidism caused by prolonged hospitalization. If anyone took an interest in this "back-ward" patient, he would first need to rehabilitate the patient as a human being. He

would have to remotivate him. He would have to manage
dependency in such a way that the patient could move out of
the hospital, and only then would it be possible to take up
his treatment. Certainly, the patient cannot improve significantly in the hospital. Since he now appears to have regressed
and to have become unmotivated, however, no one is interested
in discharging him from the hospital. It is in this dilemma
that the patient exists at the present time. He is terribly sick
and totally nonfunctional. Each day in the hospital his disabilities increase, and if given enough time he will become a
patient with such severe "hospitalitis" that he will live a
totally "crazy" existence.

Ferd Hudson was referred by his local physician for consultation because of his complaints of nervousness and of
intractable pain in his lower abdomen. Early in the first hour
of consultation, Mr. Hudson revealed a history of severe and
incapacitating pain with shifting locus that had persisted since
age forty-nine. At the time of the referral he was fifty-nine
years old. During this ten-year period, many treatment interventions had been attempted, from placebo medications to
surgery. Twelve surgical procedures—some of them major—
had been performed, involving various parts of his anatomy.
He had had six exploratory laparotomies and various other
surgeries, including a tonsillectomy when he was fifty-four
years of age. It appeared that the physician would attack
surgically whatever site the patient was at the time complaining of as painful. Soon after each surgery—indeed, sometimes
during the postsurgical recovery in the hospital—the patient
would experience excruciating and incapacitating pain anew.

Obviously these symptoms and the treatments for them
made it impossible for Mr. Hudson to work. He had had a
long and effective work history as a tool and die maker in a
steel foundry until age forty-nine. I later learned that the
onset of the pain that made it impossible for him to work
occurred during the year following his wife's renewal of her

teaching credential. She had taken this step in order to be able to provide for herself and her husband "if he should become unable to work." The couple had reared one child, a daughter, who married early and left home a few years before the onset of the patient's pain.

By the time that he presented himself for consultation, the pattern of the patient's daily life was one of complete inactivity, boredom, and depression, punctuated by bouts of pain unrelieved by anything in which he could take an interest. The couple had given up their home and were living in a trailer, which they had located near the wife's employment. Detailed examination of the patient's thought processes was made difficult by his inability to say more than a few words without exclaiming over the degree of pain that he was experiencing. It did not appear, however, that there were major signs of loosened association or of other thought pathology. Thematic content of his verbalizations centered around the ambivalence that he felt at being dependent on his wife, on doctors, and on the world in general.

A conference with the referring physician made it apparent that he was eager to have me undertake the patient's care because nothing that he had done seemed to make any difference in the patient's response to his chronic condition. I agreed to see Mr. Hudson once each week, provided that the referring physician would continue to prescribe for the patient (after he and I had agreed upon an appropriate chemotherapeutic intervention), and we agreed that I would structure my contacts with the patient as his major medical resource, with the referring physician acting as the family doctor to whom the patient would return when the patient and the psychotherapist agreed that his sort of medical intervention was called for.

The patient kept his appointments faithfully, insisting that he pay in cash at the end of each therapy hour. Early in the contacts, the patient and I worked out together, and the patient wrote down, a detailed structuring of the distribution of his time and effort during the week. This plan involved getting up at a particular hour of the day, making breakfast for his wife and himself, walking five blocks to the nearest store to buy a morning paper, reading the paper until mid-morning, at which time he would then wash and dry the breakfast dishes, sweep the floors of the trailer, and so forth, in the most minute detail, so that all of each day was carefully structured and filled with activity. The patient complained bitterly that he was unable to adhere to this schedule because of the excruciating pain to which he was subject, but I insisted that these were goals that we must work toward. I offered him the conceptualization that much of his discomfort came from not accustoming his body to the useful and productive expenditure of effort, and I suggested that, although the pain might well persist, he would find it more bearable and manageable if he could adhere to the kind of schedule that we had outlined. After four or five visits in which his complaint of pain dominated the time that we spent together, the patient began, at first minimally and later fully, to express some pride of accomplishment in having met various aspects of the schedule.

Mrs. Hudson, who had been much concerned about the patient's pain and depression and who had accompanied him for his first few visits, began to appear reassured when another person assumed the onus of managing his daily life, and she too fairly quickly assumed comfortably the role of helping him to maintain his structured schedule and added her praise to that of the therapist on those occasions when the patient accomplished a new phase of the structured activity.

Minor exacerbations occurred from time to time in the patient's pain and in its disruption of his adherence to his schedule, and it is of interest that these exacerbations frequently followed his hearing news of an illness or accident occurring to one of the members of his widely scattered family. Nonetheless, it was apparent that the general trend was one of increasing (although limited) functioning, with less preoccupation regarding his pain, and of more generally satisfying interpersonal relationships in his marriage and with the friends from whom the couple had become almost entirely alienated. This period of successful supportive care was interrupted when the patient and his wife were suddenly called across the United States to the side of a dying brother of the patient's, and a considerable period of time was consumed in the details of arranging the brother's estate after his death. Just before the patient's return it was unexpectedly necessary for me to leave town for a two-week period, and the patient found himself unable to reach me.

When I did return it was to learn that the patient had suffered a severe psychotic depressive reaction, manifested by somatic delusions, feelings of worthlessness, and an almost total loss of contact with reality. It had been necessary to hospitalize him in a psychiatric hospital. Here, fortunately, his case was assigned to a colleague of mine who practices supportive care of the type that we describe in this book. The patient was hospitalized for a ten-day period, and the principal element in the treatment was a full program of activities of a highly nongratifying nature, a program that was managed with strict insistence on compliance with a schedule. I visited the patient and his wife on one occasion during his hospitalization, and it was agreed that it would now be appropriate for the new therapist to continue the supportive care. Upon the patient's release from the hospital, he was encouraged by his new therapist to resume the regime that he had followed before his severe depression. Some nine months have now elapsed since his release from the hospital, and it would be fair to say that his level of functioning is somewhat better than it was at any point during the initial phase of supportive care before hospitalization. He now not only discharges the small responsibilities of his daily routine, but he has established a variety of meaningful relationships with retired men of his own age in which he can represent himself with some pride as a person who has rehabilitated himself from a severe illness to the point where he can now maintain a rather full program of activities.

To my thinking, this case represents an example of the ease with which therapeutic allegiances can be transferred in supportive care. It also represents the strict necessity for adhering to a schedule of highly structured doctor-patient contact. I believe that I committed a significant clinical error in not insisting that this patient maintain telephone contact with me on the same weekly basis during his absence away from town attending his brother's funeral. Had I done so, I could also have helped him to anticipate my two-week absence on his return. (It is always wise to have a colleague who is skilled in supportive care who can be on call to your supportive-care patients during an absence, as well as to communicate fully to each patient the length of your absence and specific instructions as to how he can contact the doctor on call, should he desire to do so.)

It is easy to imagine that this patient's rather sudden and severe psychotic depression, had it been handled in the way that has been traditional, might have led to his hospitalization in a situation of custodial care where his lack of functioning would have been expected and fostered by the hospital milieu. Had this situation occurred, there is little question in my mind that he might well have become a chronic invalid, condemned to live out the remainder of his years as a hospital patient and deprived of the opportunity for demonstrating to himself and to those people significant in his life that he is able to exercise the abilities to function that remain to him. Fortunately, as I have said, these events did not transpire; he continues in excellent supportive care in which the therapist's primary goal is to prevent further deterioration of functioning and, as some growth of self-esteem has occurred, to help him to return to the admittedly minimal level of functioning that characterized an earlier stage of his chronic illness.

Blanche Fall, a thirty-one-year-old kindergarten teacher who was born in New Jersey and who was of Protestant background, was the third of five children. She first contacted me in 1958 because she was constantly frightened by feelings that her husband of the past four years was attempting to poison her. She had had previous treatment one year earlier for approximately eighty hours on the couch, during which she showed marked exacerbation of all of her problems.

Her symptoms consisted of feeling that other people were against her, that she could not function, and that she could not concentrate. She had a multitude of somatic complaints. She was unable to have comfortable sexual relations with her husband, and she constantly felt guilty. On her first contact with me she reported a dream that her father had a heart attack and died and that she was then herself dying and was buried with her father. She expressed many feelings of worthlessness, stating that she did not feel that she could afford psychotherapy. She related that her husband was unwilling to pay the bills and that she could not function in school. She had stopped working as a full-time schoolteacher approximately two years before; she had attempted substitute teaching but had been unable to continue functioning in this capacity for the past six months. Many difficulties had arisen in school. She felt that the principal and the other teachers were against her, and eventually she thought that they were attempting to poison her. During the initial contact the husband was seen, a schizoid, rigid person who maintained a great distance between himself and his wife. He seemed genuinely interested in her but could not really offer her much support. He felt upset by his wife's "temper tantrums" and thought that all she had to do was to "pull herself together." He felt that she had been the same way all her life, and he did not understand why she was having psychotherapy or what good it had done her in the past. The initial diagnosis was schizophrenic reaction, paranoid type, which was corroborated in a telephone contact with the previous therapist. He had discontinued her treatment because she had felt that she could not afford regular therapy and also because he had felt that it was not progressing.

I began treatment after the initial interview with the patient and her husband by outlining in detail what would be required of both the patient and the therapist. She was told that she would be seen once a week; that she would engage in certain kinds of activities; that she would not need medication. She was also told that a long period of treatment would be required, which would evolve eventually into improved functioning on her part. During the next two years she was seen regularly once a week. Each time that I pushed for increased responsibility on her part, she showed mild exacerbation of symptoms. In little more than a month after beginning treatment, she lost all of her paranoid symptoms, seemed to feel much more comfortable, and began to approach her husband with demands for more closeness. He reacted by withdrawing further, and a number of fights ensued. The patient, however, seemed to manage them quite well and eventually came to believe that it was her husband who needed treatment. At this point, the husband too felt that he needed some help, because he was no longer able to cope with his wife's demands for increased closeness. I referred him to another therapist, who also saw him as schizoid and who treated him with supportive care.

The patient continued to improve and functioned very well —so well, in fact, that after approximately a year I began to doubt the correctness of my diagnosis. To all intents and purposes she was intact; there was no evidence of the schizophrenia. She had again taken up substitute teaching and at the end of a year of psychotherapy accepted a regular job as a kindergarten teacher. A number of minor crises occurred, but she apparently was able to handle them with the support that I offered her. Because of my growing doubt about the initial diagnosis, I felt that perhaps she required not supportive care but intensive expressive psychotherapy to resolve some of her neurotic symptoms. Her complaints at this time consisted of not getting close enough to people and not really being able to deal with feelings. She wanted to be treated on the couch and she wanted to be seen three times a week. I agreed to treat her more intensively, and we began working with some of her dreams. Within two appointments the underlying major psychopathology became clear. During the second session she suddenly confessed that she felt that her husband was making poison sandwiches for her. She had been unable to go to school since her first session on the couch, had been totally preoccupied with the material discussed from the dream, and had developed concern over some homosexual feelings toward another teacher. We continued in expressive psychotherapy for one more appointment, for which she arrived poorly groomed, grossly delusional, and experiencing auditory hallucinations. It became apparent that although the underlying schizophrenic process had been so well covered up that I had begun to doubt my own diagnosis, it was very much there. As soon as I dealt with her by confrontation and interpretation, her behavior and functioning became totally disorganized. I quickly switched tactics and returned to the once-a-week appointment, sat her up in a chair, and again focused on activity, on reality, on the here and now, and on her functioning. Within two weeks she returned to the previous level of remission and continued to function very well. During the next two years she continued in supportive psychotherapy. Eventually she decided that she and her husband could buy a house. A minor crisis occurred at the time of this purchase, which represented a stress of increased responsibility and resulted in a mild exacerbation of symptoms, including two sleepless nights, disturbing dreams, and some feelings of unreality. As she dealt with the feeling of responsibility over the house, as she was able to face the fact that certain things were more difficult for her than for other people, the symptoms went into remission and she continued to function well.

Approximately six months after the crisis over the purchase of the house, the patient was working regularly and had settled down in her own home. The relationship with the husband improved. At this point, contact was decreased to once a month, with the understanding that if anything came up the patient was welcome to call the therapist at any time. The patient continued on the once-a-month basis for the following year, functioning well. She demonstrated ability to relate to other people, became active in the teachers' organization, and in fact showed no remnants of her major mental illness. At this point an unplanned pregnancy occurred. The patient considered having an abortion and also considered the possibility of going ahead with the pregnancy. She was seen on a weekly basis in connection with this crisis. A detailed discussion followed in regard to her ability to function as a mother. She reviewed many of the problems that she had had with her own mother, but made the decision jointly with her husband to go ahead with the pregnancy. She had many fears about exacerbation of her symptoms, and it was decided jointly by the patient and me that throughout the pregnancy and until several months after the baby was born she would be seen on a once-a-week basis. During this time, however, she did not show any exacerbation of symptoms and continued to function well.

Just before the delivery the patient did have a few frightening dreams, some mild depressive symptoms, and great concern about the possibility of becoming mentally ill, but she went into delivery very comfortably, and I visited her in the hospital. During my visit I noted that she was quite happy and had no major difficulties. During the immediate post-partum period, I saw her on two occasions at her regular appointment time in her home, and then subsequently she was able to return to the office for regular weekly appointments. Within a period of ten weeks post partum, it became clear that she was doing quite well and that she was able to handle the child appropriately. She decided to return to her teaching. She hired a very able baby-sitter and went back to her job. At this point psychotherapy was again scheduled on a monthly basis. Six months later her husband was transferred to a job in Kansas and the patient was referred to a therapist to continue supportive care there. She decided, however, not to establish a psychotherapeutic relationship there but only to have the name available in case of emergency. Instead, she wrote a letter to me approximately once a month, to which I replied essentially expressing interest and reassurance. On one occasion during her year in Kansas she came to Los Angeles and made an appointment. She and I reviewed a very satisfactory adjustment in Kansas. After having spent a year in Kansas, she returned to Los Angeles with her family, went back to teaching, and continued to function very well. In the meantime, her husband had completed his treatment. After her return from Kansas, regular therapy was not scheduled, but she was told that she should see me twice a year and that she could call for an appointment. On this basis we have continued for the past few years. She comes in twice a year to review events. In addition, I receive a mimeographed Christmas letter that she sends to all of her friends. I send her a reply to this letter, stating that I notice that she is getting along well and that I continue to be interested and concerned. It is on this basis that the case has continued for the past three years of the eight years of supportive care. The patient is contented, is functioning well, has had no exacerbation of symptoms, and has used the supportive care minimally. She continues to need the knowledge of the therapist's availability and reassures herself about it by appointments twice a year and one Christmas letter. No major crises have occurred, and the patient is living a satisfactory, full life as a teacher, a mother, and a wife.

Betty Gower is now twenty-two years old. She was the last of three children born to lower middle class parents in a suburb of New York. The parents' marriage was not a stable one, and on at least one occasion the mother left for several months to live in the South, while the children remained in New York. When Mrs. Gower was five years old, her father suddenly died of a heart attack during his sleep. The mother,

who had always been a rather aggressive, driving, and domi-
nating woman, placed the children in Catholic boarding
schools in Texas and moved to Texas herself, where she en-
tered the business world. While the mother advanced through
a series of successful positions in real estate the children were
placed in a series of boarding schools, all of which Mrs. Gower
remembers as being highly inhibiting and restrictive in the
attitudes of the nuns who staffed them. When Mrs. Gower
was twelve the mother took the children out of boarding
school and brought them to live with her when she established a residence with a man in another city in Texas. This
period lasted only a few months, after which the mother decided to marry her friend and move the children to California.

During her childhood, Mrs. Gower remembers being
quite reserved, somewhat shy, having few close friends, and
being concerned about other people's opinions of her.

There was a brief period at age fourteen when Mrs.
Gower began to "run with a wild crowd," which involved her
sneaking out of the house at night and traveling with a group
of girls to various parties where they would drink. This activity ceased when Mrs. Gower's mother discovered it and
forbade it. Although remarried, the mother continued to work
in real estate and to achieve financial success. Her marriage
was not a happy one, and she was out of the house a great
deal of the time. Mrs. Gower became the housekeeper for her
stepfather and his mother and her two brothers, and she
would come home from school to spend much time busying
herself around the house. She remembers her high school
years as not particularly happy. For one rather protracted
period she worked as a mother's helper, which kept her away
from her own family almost entirely. She had a good relationship with the young couple for whom she worked, and she
developed a schoolgirl crush on the father of the household.

During these high school years she was quite sexually
inhibited; the only sexual contact was minor sex play with a
little boy in the neighborhood. She has continued to feel very

guilty about this incident. As she began to date she indulged in perhaps less than the usual amount of adolescent petting, until her final year of high school, when she met Mr. Gower. Mr. Gower is a few years older than she, and by that time he had finished high school and was working as a grocery clerk. He too was from a Catholic family, although neither Mrs. Gower nor he was very deeply involved in religious observances. A rather intense relationship grew between them (including a sexual relationship in which Mrs. Gower behaved in what was—for her—an unusually uninhibited way).

Shortly after she graduated from high school they were married. All during the premarital sexual relationship there had been no attempt at contraception, but after marriage Mrs. Gower began to use an oral contraceptive. Mr. Gower, after only a month or two of marriage, began to show symptoms of gastrointestinal disease, which was treated symptomatically by the family physician. At this point the couple decided to have a child and stopped using contraceptives. Mrs. Gower soon became pregnant; almost immediately thereafter Mr. Gower's symptoms increased markedly in their severity, and he became acutely ill. It was soon determined that he would require major abdominal surgery. Mrs. Gower, who had been employed since her graduation from high school as a clerk, gave up her job and took over the full-time day and night nursing care of her gravely ill husband. The members of Mr. Gower's family were much impressed with Mrs. Gower's fortitude in carrying through her pregnancy and providing excellent total care for her husband, and they gave her much praise. As the pregnancy approached term, Mr. Gower's condition improved, and he began to resume his responsibilities as husband and provider just as his wife's pregnancy was successfully terminated.

It was at this point that Mrs. Gower first became aware of a serious emotional disturbance in herself. When she came home from the hospital with her new son, she felt totally overwhelmed by the responsibility and unable to discharge it successfully. When the baby cried, even though she had fed him and changed his diaper and had done everything else she could think of to stop the crying, she would then lose her temper and spank him, after which she would feel overwhelmingly guilty. She would frequently tell her husband that she was unable to care for the child, and he would take over the motherly tasks and perform them successfully. Mrs. Gower would then feel even more worthless and desperate. During the times when she had abandoned her responsibilities for the child to her husband or to her mother-in-law, she would drive aimlessly around in her car, overwhelmed by her feelings of inadequacy, guilt, and shame.

At about this time, she made a suicidal gesture and was taken to a psychiatric hospital, where she spent one week. She participated only minimally in the therapeutic program of the hospital, and she did not tell her doctor or her fellow patients any of the details about which she was so concerned. Upon her release from the hospital, the same pattern continued at home, although her interpersonal relationships were deteriorating. Over some objections from her husband, she arranged to leave the son with her mother-in-law and resume working. Although she got some sense of accomplishment and achievement from her employment, she continued to feel worthless as a mother and wife and began to have major symptoms of mental illness.

She experienced periods of ideational confusion. She also experienced massive anxiety, which she interpreted as gastric distress, and she began hallucinating. Mrs. Gower was at this time about twenty years old. After her marriage, she had begun to take her medical problems to the general practitioner who was physician to her husband and his family. Because she always identified her problems as physical ones, he would pursue a physical line of inquiry into her ailments. The anxiety that she experienced as a "stomach cramp" occasioned a series of abdominal X-rays. A kinked ureter was visualized and was presumed to be the source of her pain. At this time she did not see, as she later did, the temporal relationship between the pain and stressful situations. Another of her responses to anxiety was confusion. There were increasingly frequent and increasingly prolonged periods during which she could not "make her thoughts work right." Her mind seemed blank, and she was unable to concentrate on the task at hand. The first hallucination occurred and took the form of seeing herself damaged, mutilated, or injured in a variety of situations.

Mrs. Gower reported none of these mental phenomena to anyone and took her physical complaints to the family doctor. As time wore on it became increasingly obvious to her husband and his family and to the family doctor that she was showing signs of severe emotional disturbance, and they began to recommend to her that she hospitalize herself. She resisted the suggestions, indeed became angry when they were made, and eventually in a sort of crisis of desperation she precipitated a marital separation. During this period she had one brief extramarital affair, and her symptoms rapidly became worse, to the point where bizarre behavior necessitated her husband's physically taking her to the psychiatric hospital, where she admitted herself.

The treatment program there involved an enforced participation in a therapeutic milieu that was rich in activity, and she also was on a program of chemotherapy and group and individual psychotherapy. Her hallucinations increased in frequency during the first month of her hospitalization. Her individual therapist was a first-year resident in psychiatry. I was the group therapist. When in three months she had not made any significant improvement and upon the resident's rotation off the service, I took over her care. She was discharged from the hospital some two weeks later, continued on the chemotherapeutic regime which had been begun in the hospital, and was seen once a week for one hour in supportive care.

In her aftercare visits she was reminded of the discovery that she had made while she was in the hospital that involving herself in a structured activity was a means through which she could master ideational confusion. Furthermore, it was stressed that such attempts at mastery were important to her because the confusion invariably preceded the terrifying hallucinatory experiences. As she improves in her functioning, and as periods of confusion become more infrequent and last for shorter intervals, she has a tendency to introduce more abstractions, such as "Do normal people feel guilty about thinking harmful thoughts?" I make sure that I remind her, at such times as these, that what counts is how she behaves—not how she thinks or feels. Always the emphasis is on action.

It has now been two years since her initial discharge from the hospital. During this time there have been several exacerbations in the degree of her symptomatology, and she has been hospitalized on nine occasions, the longest for seventeen days and the shortest for one day. She has learned to be sensitive to the relative severity of her symptoms, and as they increase she seeks additional support by telephone. The initial dosage of medication with which she began the aftercare phase of her treatment was reduced and, although it has been modified on a few occasions of exacerbation, she is now on a minimal dosage of phenothiazine once daily.

She demonstrates well the point made earlier in this book that medication can serve as a talisman or symbol of the therapeutic relationship, for she always carries three or four pills with her, replacing them as the coating wears off and they disintegrate. Also, she feels anxious unless she takes the medication, but the anxiety is relieved some ten minutes after ingesting the pills—long before this response could be due to any pharmacologic effect.

The supportive relationship has become an important element in her life and in the life of her family. She frequently comes to her therapeutic hour accompanied by her husband and child, and I sometimes see them. She is providing excellent care for her child, and she is performing her wifely duties in an exemplary manner. She tends to be rather conservative and quite compulsive in carrying out her tasks, and these attitudes are encouraged in her supportive care. There have been some stormy episodes in her relationship with her mother—indeed, they have frequently precipitated her exacerbations—but she has now learned not to be so much disturbed by things that her mother continues to do and that have always disturbed her.

The most recent exacerbation of her illness seems to be related to an attempt that she and her husband made to have another child. It became evident that she was highly ambivalent about such a step; she dreaded being again confronted by the responsibility that she had handled so poorly the first time, yet she felt obligated to provide her husband with more children and her son with a sibling. As she became more self-recriminatory regarding her dislike of becoming pregnant, she began to have self-destructive thoughts. It was when she lost her controls and hurt herself (in a minor but symbolically important way) that it was decided to hospitalize her again. She can now begin to see the hospital in the way that so many successful supportive care patients see it—"It's a good place to stay away from, yet it's good to know it's there when I start to take action on my bad thoughts and don't control them."

As she was helped to see that her self-esteem was not dependent on her role as a bearer of offspring, she began to be more sure of her behavioral controls. She has now resumed contraception and is pleased to state "I'm not going to have any more children—or even if I do, it won't be too bad if I wait eight or ten more years." She need not meet a demand that she perceived in the expectancies of her husband and others, yet she succeeds in maintaining an openness to her future.

There seems little doubt that Mr. Gower's supportive care has made a significant alteration in the course that her illness would have taken had she continued to be hospitalized for a lengthy period in the manner that was traditional at her hospital. Indeed, a good deal of the therapeutic effort that has been applied in her case was necessitated by the increasing alienation that was occurring in the patient's life as a result of her three-month hospitalization. There are many helpful people in this woman's life, and part of the therapeutic task has been to help these people to regain their confidence in her ability to re-establish good self-control and to redevelop the mutually rewarding relationships that she had with them before the onset of her severe illness. Mrs. Gower now represents a good example of the kind of outcome that successful supportive care can have. She is aware that her present good feeling is something that she has won for herself and that can be maintained only by a realistic and vigilant attitude toward her behavioral responses. She still occasionally asks, "How long will you be my doctor?" to which I invariably respond, "So long as you need me, and, since it's obvious that we are helping you by keeping up these appointments, let's not be in a hurry to terminate them." In other words, one of the reasons why this treatment can be looked upon as successful is precisely because it is still continuing.

16

The Experience of Illness

◆◆◆

After extensive initial training from his teachers and from his books, and after mastery of the theories of etiology and the techniques of intervention, the clinician finally recognizes that he can learn only from his patients. Long ago, great teachers of medicine suggested to their students that, when in doubt, they throw away their books and theories and sit by the patient's bedside to observe, to learn, and to understand. We have spent many hours listening to thousands of patients, each one describing his own personal world of agony and despair. From these descriptions by our patients we are gradually understanding chronic mental illness. The many symptoms that are easily described clinically as thought process disorder, impaired reality testing, shallow interpersonal relationships, and defective ego functioning do not adequately portray the despair and distress of our patients, for which they seek help and in which the therapist must intervene. In this chapter we have collected a number of descriptions given by patients of their various states of distress and despair. None of these descriptions is offered as diagnostic of any one illness. They are given by a variety of patients with various conditions, but all of them have in common the description of the distress and agony with which a patient comes to us for help. Patients do not come with a diagnosis; they come with pain and suffering. They do not come with an illness; they come with a plea for intervention that will give them relief.

A compassionate understanding of these words by patients, which describe various states of distress, will help the therapist to clarify the nature of the disease and the requirements for the intervention. In fact, many of the techniques and procedures described in this book make sense only when the therapist understands the true nature of the chaos within the patient. To talk about the technique of providing a constant, consistent, and never-ending therapeutic relationship makes sense only after we have understood the agony of the loneliness and emptiness of the patient suffering from the panic of depersonalization. Only then does it become clear how the therapist's constant and consistent availability becomes a therapeutic beacon which lights the way as the patient claws his way out of the pit of despair. Although many of the descriptions given in this chapter may sound unclinical and unscientific and may even seem melodramatic and exaggerated, these are all actual words spoken by patients in describing the experience of being mentally ill.

In the following pages we have classified these descriptions under ten general headings. Obviously, many of these states of discomfort blend with each other and are only artificially separated for purposes of this discussion. It is difficult, for example, to tell where emptiness leaves off and loneliness begins, since both are closely related to feelings of worthlessness and hopelessness, resulting in a partial alienation of the human being from his fellow man and from his world. The states of confusion, disorganization, and depersonalization create feelings of panic and thus are closely linked with each other in the patient's subjective experience of his illness. We should like to remind those of our readers who reject these descriptions as unscientific and too subjective that the words and behavior of the patient represent the real data of psychiatry. The scientific language and the jargon of our field belong to us, not to the patient. Scientific terms merely represent an attempt by one clinician to communicate with another about the observations he has made of his patients. The data for all of our scientific terminology come from descriptions such as these, that is to say, from observations of both verbal and nonverbal behavior.

The isolation that the patient feels from his fellow man, which results in feelings of *alienation,* is vividly described by our patients. Such alienation leads to much pain, since the patient always feels alone, outside, and unattached. He almost literally does not feel himself a member of the human race.

"I am like a zombie living behind a glass wall. I can see all that goes on in the world but I can't touch it. I can't reach it. I can't be in contact with it. I am outside. They are inside and when I get inside, they aren't there. There is nothing there, absolutely nothing."

"Take what you want and let me go
I only ask of you, Be quick, Be quick!
Do not explore this frozen continent." (S.F.)

"I am living a make-believe life and fear I'm being asked to pretend even more. It is a real fantasy. It has all the horrors of the fantastic. Should I find myself by giving up myself? Is it, instead, that myself must change, must become 'lovely'?"

"It is an appearance that I now can only maintain at times, that I am being asked not only to adopt but to replace myself with. I'm different, too. Can't fit into another's pattern. Most people seem to fit into a sort of group pattern but mine is the absolute of such, it seems. I'm not this or that, so easily classified as others wish me to be and usually it is their classification they wish me to fit. They call this 'caring,' 'loving' me."

"There's something wrong with me. I don't seem to feel about my family like others do. I notice when I talk about my wife and children, I talk about them like my neighbors talk about their cars. Sure, I'm proud of them, just like they are of their cars and I like them, but if they all went away it wouldn't bother me. They are really quite dispensable. I would just get somebody new, just like my neighbors get their new cars."

"We forgot that we were not that which we wish to be. We thought then the shame and saw the difference only in others and then scorned them. But now, it is I who scorns myself and you; and not the others any more. It wasn't vanity, for that pertains to something one has and we have not. We're not that which we choose and by forgetting, denying the truth, we cease to exist. Because we are not identical with our vision of ourselves, we deny even our own real existence. You see how I kill myself, murder myself, by believing myself to be other than I am?"

"To me, the world is peopled, rather than populated. What I mean by peopled is that it is filled with people; much like to others houses are furnished with furniture. It is all the same to me."

From such alienation comes a *panic* of major proportions. The patient feels outside of the human race. He is all alone. He has no real identity, and nowhere can he touch another human being. He is in panic.

"I'm so scared of doing things and yet want to cram so much in. But I lack the courage to give up; yet, I can't go ahead and change. This whole life seems to be getting ready to die. I'm not ready yet, and I'm so afraid of what will happen, and you are pushing me to get ready by forgetting like so many people do. Then they die before they use themselves up. The only way I can use myself up is to give myself away. But you and most people don't want what I have to give away. You want me to appear to be exactly as you pretend to be, to affirm your pretext existence rather than to contribute my own. If only you would give me your real self. I am greedy to enrich my preparation and to accept my real self. Then we would both share in a doubled existence; add another person and it is trebled."

"I don't know what makes me tick
I don't know what makes me sick
This dying feeling's what I dread
And I keep wishing I were dead." (S.F.)

"I am not yet sure how much control I have over impulses and maybe that's why my husband is so protective. I've caught myself staring, on occasions, and wanting to go on spending sprees, and eating more than I should, but the really frightening symptoms of the past periods when I would have to go cling to the wall have not recurred. I'm so thankful that, believe me, I haven't forgotten and never will let myself forget to be aware of the danger line."

"When I was acting so stiff and wasn't talking, it was because I had the feeling that if I moved the whole world might collapse. I knew what you were saying, I knew what was going on in the room around me, but I didn't dare budge an inch. I don't know why, but I seemed like I was at the center of everything and everything depended on my not moving. It was such a terrible relief when I could begin to lose the feeling that I was so important. I think it wasn't until after you stopped paying so much attention to me that I could stop thinking I was so important. Because when you were paying so much attention to me, it made me feel that I was extra important, and it sort of added to the feeling I had."

"It starts like a feeling of pressure in the back of my neck and head, and then the pressure sort of spreads all over and I feel like I am a bomb that is about to go off. It's like if I looked at myself in the mirror I'd be all puffed up and be colored a bright red. That's when it's hardest to think clear and nobody seems to understand how close I am to blowing up, but I guess the worst is the times when I do blow up. I feel so damn awful after I have done something like broken something or destroyed something. If only I could keep myself from going that far. But before, there wasn't anybody who seemed to know that I am such a dangerous guy."

Many of our patients express the feeling of *emptiness*. Such feelings are tremendously painful to the patient and result in the feelings of worthlessness and loneliness described by others.

"What right have you got to tell me that I shouldn't kill myself? Isn't my life mine to do with what I want? If it was any kind of life, it would be a different story, but I can't really ever remember feeling that I was a person whom people ought to be considerate about. I remember my mother used to talk right past me, as if I weren't there. And even now, when I do all the things I'm supposed to do for my daughter and my husband, it isn't really like they were reacting to me like a person. More like a machine that does mother things and wife things. It doesn't seem like they, or my mother, or anybody ever built anything into me. I guess I just started off empty and stayed empty and all of the busy work that goes on in living what people call life doesn't seem to stick— doesn't seem to last. And besides, I don't see why—as big a nothing as I am—you should consider me worth bothering about or worth trying to keep me from killing myself. You don't really convince me that you care."

"Nothing is me. Nothing is mine.
I don't live in my body.
I don't live anywhere.
My body just is.
It is like the strings are pulled
And it is moved automatically.
But I haven't anything in it."

"There is a big hole in my chest. It is so empty it hurts, in fact, it is going to explode with emptiness. It is an agony. It simply is that I have to stick something in it. I feel like I have to take a knife or a stick and poke it into my chest to try to fill the emptiness. This big emptiness in me is going to implode."

"Who am I?
I shift with every change in wind
Sometimes cool, sometimes kind
Sometimes young, sometimes old
Sometimes warm, too often cold
Though I dig deep in every you
Trying to pull out what's true
For all of us, it is you I see
I can't find me." (S.F.)

"I feel like I am a thin, empty shell. There is a huge gaping hole in my body. No matter how much I pour into it, it never fills. It never gets any stronger. It's like an eggshell which is empty."

"I don't have any feelings. I have nothing except the ache of emptiness."

From such alienation and from such emptiness comes the *loneliness* and the fear of reaching out to others. From this loneliness comes one of the great therapeutic difficulties in managing the chronic schizophrenic patient. He generally has given up trying to break out of his loneliness by reaching out to other human beings for help.

"She sang softly and sobbed silently, so alone, so alone. Who cares or wants her? Shriveled and torn, so alone, wet, cold, like a smelly corpse. So alone. Shouting for help. No one can hear. No one can help."

"People are fun but the upkeep is awful—you have to care about them."

"Right and wrong
Blame and guilt
The flow of love
Is choked by silt." (S.F.)

And then we see the patient's *disorganization* appearing as he struggles with such feelings of loneliness.

"It just feels like something is dragging my seeds down, and like if I don't hold on to my belly, my guts will fall out. Sometimes I realize that this couldn't happen, but the feeling is so strong that it is easy to forget that it wouldn't really happen. Then, if I make myself do the chores you told me to get done, it seems to help me to be more realistic about those physical feelings in my insides. It isn't that the pain goes away—I'm still aware of it, but doing something real with my hands seems to make my thoughts more real. But I want you to know that this is an awful strong feeling. It's pretty hard to keep myself convinced that those terrible things aren't going to happen."

"Everything seems so mixed up—so disorganized. I can't seem to fit anything into place or put my finger on anything. I can't seem to make my thoughts follow one another logically —I just sit in a kind of confused muddle. It's a funny, drifting kind of feeling—but not a pleasant drifting, I mean. And then in a way, it's almost like a relief if I start to hallucinate. At least I don't just sit confused—I kind of pay attention to what I am hallucinating. Even though it scares hell out of me, and I can talk about it now like I knew it was hallucination, when it really happens I don't know. I'm not at all sure. It's just like things were unreal in my confusion and then they suddenly become real when the experience happens that I am now later calling hallucinations."

The *depersonalization* the patients describe adds to the pain and agony.

"I look like a human being, but I'm really not. I'm just a make-believe."

"I'm making family out of strangers and I'm making strangers out of my family."

"I look at my arms and they aren't mine. They move without my direction. Somebody else moves them. All my limbs and my thoughts are attached to strings, and these strings are pulled by others, I know not who. I have no control. I don't live in me. The outside and I are all the same."

One of the most common cries of pain results from the feelings of *worthlessness* that almost all patients describe at times.

"I feel like a smoldering pile of shit."

"Even though I'm supposedly a healthy young man, no woman wants me. I used the computer last night to look at my problem. After calculating the present population of adult men and women over the age of eighteen and below the age of fifty and then looking up some sizes of sexual organs in medical books, I discovered that there are approximately 24,600 kilometers of unused vagina in the United States every night and there isn't even six inches for me anywhere. It's hopeless."

"Peggy Shit sits to spit, stare and starve.
She sits solemnly, scorned and so—so separated from science."

"Life is a large ass and quarreling parents, all covered with a large bowel movement."

"Shit stinks smelly. Fat rats scat. Peggy sits alone and shouts.
Alone, shoes smell.
She stinks so alone and is so scared."

The *confusion* from all of these feelings is described as:

"When I have words the feeling will not come
But when I truly feel, I'm dumb." (S.F.)

"I woke up this morning and I knew that it wasn't a world which was upside down or inside out. It was my eyes. They completely turned in the socket. Everything was backward and inverted. Everything moved that shouldn't move. Everything that should move, stood still. There was lots of noise and no sense."

Hopelessness is the natural consequence of the alienation, the emptiness, the loneliness, and the feelings of worthlessness. There is little to keep the future open—to kindle the flame of hope.

"Last night I finally had the chance to put my penis in a lady. It was all nothing. The whole thing is nothing. It isn't much, that's for sure. I'm not going to do it any more. Never again. There is nothing there. There's absolutely nothing."

"Where I am there is no peace
Anger is my one release
It boomerangs in words that burn
And punish me when they return." (S.F.)

"I'm a frozen body in a frozen continent. Nothing moves. I stay away from people because if they push me hard or pull me hard, my frozen limbs will break off. There is a quiet noise inside of me. I think it is my soul. It still stirs once in a while. It isn't frozen all of the way, but I know soon I will break."

"The curtain going down is caught between
The dingy ceiling and the dusty floor
Although the stage is bare
We sit as if something were there
Still to be seen
We were the actors and the audience
The authors, too.
Now the play is through

Our recompense
Is nothing, nothing, less than nothing
What did we gain
For twenty years
Bitterness and pain
And tears
For what we might have been and what we are
Yet we sit afraid to leave
The futile make-believe." (S.F.)

From utter *despair* our patients reach out for relief and intervention.

"Our cat has kittens
The trees are in leaf
But all I produce
Is more grief." (S.F.)

"There is nothing left. Everything is dark and darkness. I cannot live. I can't die. I cannot move. I'm completely stuck. My feet are in the quicksand. I do not understand. I do not go under, I do not get up. I cannot get free. I'm stuck, stuck, stuck."

"Who feels the black fists of despair
Squeezing the heart
Is my counterpart
Yet the heart beats
Despite defeats
Sometimes races, sometimes slows
But it goes
This plodding victory is too much to bear." (S.F.)

These outcries of agony in the patient's words describe his subjective experience of being emotionally disturbed and mentally ill. No matter what the official classification of the illness, nor what the technical clinical descriptions of the states, the patient's own words best describe the feelings of

alienation and panic, of emptiness and loneliness, of disorganization and depersonalization, of worthlessness and confusion,
and of the utter hopelessness and despair that the patient
brings to us, asking for help and for intervention. It is in the
patient's words that we can understand the agony. It is from
the patient's words that we can recognize the true significance
of the treatment intervention. It is from these words that we
can learn the techniques of supportive care.

Glossary

The following list of phrases represents a terminology which we have evolved in discussing and in teaching our concept of supportive care. These phrases are not drawn from any standard text of diagnosis or therapeutics; rather, we found them useful precisely because they avoid the connotations of standard terminology and have the freshness of non-technical talk. A number of these phrases were suggested by Vincent Mazzanti, M.D., whose papers are referred to in the bibliography.

to drag one's feet—The therapist, by reminding the patient of the reality of his illness, helps the patient to avoid impulsive behavior or the assumption of tasks too complex or threatening for the patient's present adaptational level.

to get him off the hook—The therapist reminds the patient of alternative behavioral or perceptual choices to the one presented by the patient as appropriate. This serves to reinforce the therapist's basic acceptance of the patient and reflects the non-demanding character of the relationship.

latent language—Communication by using metaphors, thus avoiding the threat of a direct confrontation with ideas which the

238

patient cannot tolerate without losing self-esteem or the trust
of the therapist.

selective attention—In the treatment transaction the therapist, by
paying more attention to the patient's comments, which focus
on activity as opposed to fantasy and which reveal more
healthy functioning than disturbed functioning, can manage
the "hour" in such a way as to promote his supportive goals
in the relationship.

open-ended relationship—Characteristic of and essential to the
doctor-patient relationship in supportive care. Transactions are
managed by the therapist in such a way that a continuation
of the relationship indefinitely into the future is implied, even
though the "here-and-now" forms the content of most of the
conversation.

titration of dependency—After trust has been allowed to develop
in the patient toward the therapist and he thus allows himself
to depend on the therapist, he attempts to depend on reality
beyond the therapeutic transaction (after many tests of it).
Eventually he invests other persons with trust by allowing
himself to depend on them. The therapist can manage the
widening of this circle of trusting relationships by preparing
the patient for what can happen as he tentatively reaches
beyond the core relationship.

non-judgmental relationship—In supportive care the therapist cre-
ates an atmosphere in which the patient is accepted as a
person; he is not judged negatively in a moral sense, and he
is made to feel worth while. He is not held responsible for his
chaotic feelings or thoughts; he is helped to realize that he is
answerable to his fellow men for his behavior. Thus, by "selective attention" (vide supra), the therapist de-emphasizes
the inner life of the patient and helps the patient to judge the
appropriateness of his overt acts.

referring the patient to life—The only way in which the doctor-
patient relationship in supportive care "ends." The therapist,
by participating in the patient's life-planning, moves slowly
to the position of being a supportive, parental friend—a relationship which also continues into the future. Even in such an
altered relationship, the therapist must always remain availa-

ble to the patient as a former and a potential therapist, should the need arise.

reinforcing the therapeutic intent—Frequently patients behave in such a way as to reassure themselves of the reality of the therapeutic relationship and of its availability. They may telephone the therapist's office to confirm an appointment which was firmly established, or they may drive past a hospital where they were treated during a period of symptom exacerbation.

the dumping syndrome—Here used to refer to those instances in which a family or a doctor makes referral of a patient to a psychiatrist when the patient's behavior has angered and alienated them as supportive resources. Frequently the psychiatrist can support these referring sources to continue to function by encouraging ventilation of the feelings engendered by the patient's behavior and can help them to see alternative responses to the patient. When this is not possible, the psychiatrist must give the referring source a "vacation" from the responsibility by bringing to bear other sources of support.

more miles per gallon—A phrase we have found ourselves using in describing supportive care to colleagues in mental health professions. It refers to our experience that well-managed supportive care patients are a useful and gratifying part of one's practice—not a frustrating or boring part. With a minimum investment of the therapist's time, patients are helped to function in a much more effective way than they could without such care, they are saved from the suffering which they and their families would experience if they were allowed to disorganize and decompensate, and the society is not required to maintain them as a non-productive public charge. Thus, each unit of therapy time produces more effect than is the case in expressive therapy with less sick patients.

keeping the future open—A key concept in supportive care. Patients need hope, and they need to view the relationship with the therapist as one with an implied future, regardless of the vagaries of the illness. All aspects of the transaction with the patient, both obvious and tacit, must be managed with these needs of the patient continuously in mind.

entrance ticket—A phrase which refers to the behavior of the patient when he presents himself for treatment. The patient who requires supportive care has much discontent in his life; the manifestation of this discontent are protean and can assume a character which is conditioned by the expectancies by which the patient is surrounded. Thus, if the doctor whom he visits is a cardiologist whose interaction with the patient centers on heart function, the patient will elaborate much of his discontent by accepting the doctor's apparent interest in his heart and will express his concern with his disordered life by talking about his concern over his heart. As another example, the chronically psychotic patient whose reality testing is severely impaired and whose need for structure is great will, if his doctor is a psychoanalyst who encourages the patient to report dreams and feelings, conform to this expectancy; what he needs is the relationship with an accepting person, and he will pay nearly any price to obtain it. We have called this behavior on the part of a patient "presenting an entrance ticket."

Annotated Bibliography

BALINT, MICHAEL   *The Doctor, His Patient, and the Illness.* New York: International Universities Press, Inc., 1957.
Dr. Balint describes his methods of training non-psychiatrist physicians in the treatment of the chronically mentally ill patient. He uses a technique which is unrelated to ours in its theoretical conceptualization in that it leans heavily on the classical psychoanalytic model. It is related to ours in that he proposes that the cornerstone of the treatment intervention is care, concern, and hope.

BATESON, GREGORY   Minimal Requirements for a Theory of Schizophrenia. *A.M.A. Arch. Gen. Psychiat.,* 2:477–491, 1960.
Dr. Bateson proposes a theory that the etiology of schizophrenia is related to the double-bind situation in which children who receive conflicting signals from the significant adults find themselves unable to act. Although there is yet no evidence to support this theory as a basis for understanding the etiology of schizophrenia, it is clearly an observable fact that in adult schizophrenic patients ambiguous signals and confusing double-bind situations cause exacerbation of symptoms. Therefore, throughout our book we emphasize techniques which result in clear and simple instructions to the patient in which the verbal and the non-verbal content of the psychotherapeutic transaction convey the same message.

BEERS, CLIFFORD W.   *A Mind That Found Itself.* New York, Doubleday, Doran & Co., Inc., 1935.

Clifford Beers, the founder of the American Mental Hygiene Association, gives an excellent subjective description of the experience of his psychotic illness. In our approach to the treatment of patients we emphasize the importance of paying attention to the patient's description of his agony. Careful, detailed attention to observation of the patient by the therapist and by the patient himself gives us important data for use in the management of psychotherapeutic transaction. These observations take precedence over theoretical inferences in a psychotherapeutic system such as ours which is based on empiricism.

BESSELL, HAROLD, and MAZZANTI, VINCENT E.   Diagnosis of Ambulatory Schizophrenia: A Case Study. *Psychiat. Quart.*, 33:429–436, 1959.

This paper discusses schizophrenia from the point of view of patients who ask for help for relief of somatic symptoms. Frequently, schizophrenic patients are not properly diagnosed and thus subjected to somatic and surgical interventions which provide no relief and which are sometimes very harmful.

BINSWANGER, LUDWIG   Existential Analysis, Psychiatry, Schizophrenia. *J. Exist. Psychiat.*, 1:157–165, 1960.

Dr. Binswanger was the leader of European existential psychiatry. In this article he demonstrates his emphasis on exploring in detail the schizophrenic's world as a basis for understanding the illness and the treatment intervention.

BLEULER, EUGEN   *Dementia Praecox; or, the Group of Schizophrenias.* Joseph Zinkin (trans.), New York, International Universities Press, 1950.

Dr. Bleuler in the early part of the twentieth century changed the name of the syndrome from dementia praecox to schizophrenia. In this book he gives a detailed description of objective findings in schizophrenic patients. His work is important since it removed the stigma of deterioration and dementia from this group.

CANTOR, NATHANIEL   What Is a Normal Mind? *Amer. J. Orthopsychiat.*, 11:676–683, 1941.

Many papers have been written on the subject of normality. Obviously, there are a multitude of approaches to the concept of normality, including the statistical approach, the autocratically defined approach, the absence of disease, the ability to function, etc. None of these approaches is entirely satisfactory. In our book we do not attempt to deal with the concept of normality. We do, however, emphasize a treatment approach which attempts to maximize function and to minimize dysfunction.

CAPLAN, GERALD   *In Crisis Intervention.* Parad, H. (Ed.). Family Service, 1965.

Dr. Caplan is now a major spokesman for Community Psychiatry and crisis intervention. His concept of crisis intervention varies somewhat from ours, but we agree that resolution of crisis is a significant form of treatment. Even though we deal primarily with the topic of the treatment of chronic patients, we are constantly faced with crises in the lives of these patients. Thus, we have the dual task of resolving crises while at the same time providing support between crises to prepare the patient to better manage the next one.

CHASE, LOUIS S., and SILVERMAN, SAMUEL   Prognostic Criteria in Schizophrenia. *Amer. J. Psychiat.*, 98:360–368, 1941.

This article which was written in 1941 describes prognostic criteria in schizophrenia. The items mentioned are of interest not only from a historical point of view, but also by demonstrating how in the past prognosis was, in fact, determined by the treatment intervention. Essentially, the author states that if the schizophrenic patient is hospitalized frequently and for long periods of time the prognosis is poor. The author states these findings as though they were the result of the illness, not emphasizing that, in fact, the poor prognosis is the result of the treatment intervention.

COHEN, ROBERT A.   The Hospital as a Therapeutic Instrument. *Psychiatry*, 21:29–35, 1958.

Since the publication of Alfred H. Stanton and Morris S. Schwartz, *The Mental Hospital* (Basic Books, 1954), much emphasis has been placed on understanding the psychiatric hospital as a community and a social system which may be either therapeutic or anti-therapeutic. This article enumerates some of the considerations necessary to make it as therapeutic as possible and to minimize the anti-therapeutic factors.

COOPER, HOWARD N.   Problems in Application of the Basic Criteria of Schizophrenia. *Amer. J. Psychiat.*, 117:66–71, 1960.

The basic criteria for the diagnosis of schizophrenia first formulated by Eugen Bleuler, which includes (1) immobilizing ambivalence, (2) loosening of associations, (3) autism, and (4) inappropriate affect and affective blunting, are evaluated in this article. The author comes to the conclusion that insistence upon the rigid application of these criteria for a diagnosis of schizophrenia will lead both to failure to identify schizophrenia when it is present and to false identification of the disease when it is not present. We would concur with this conclusion, and we would suggest that the most useful approach to the diagnosis of schizophrenia is by a detailed review of the patient's history of interpersonal relationships.

DAVIDSON, HENRY A. Psychiatry and Euphemistic Delusion. *Amer. J. Psychiat.*, 110:310–312, 1953.

In this entertaining article, Dr. Davidson points our attention to the changing fashion in medicine and in psychiatry specifically which results in new names for old ideas. In our work we have attempted not to propose a new set of technical terms, but rather to develop an empirical approach to the treatment of patients based on clinical observations.

DEUTSCH, ALBERT *The Mentally Ill in America*. New York, Columbia University Press, 1946.

This historically important book reviews the changing attitudes toward the mentally ill in the United States. It outlines the confusion between legal, social, medical, and humanitarian approaches to the mentally ill patient.

ERIKSON, ERIK H. *Childhood and Society*. 2nd ed., New York: W. W. Norton & Co., Inc., 1963.

This book is one of the best psychiatric volumes of this century. In it Erikson elaborates concepts of personality development which we have found useful in clarifying the treatment transaction.

FLECK, STEPHEN, CORNELISON, ALICE R., NORTON, NEA., and LIDZ, THEODORE The Interaction between Hospital Staff and Families of Patients. *Psychiatry*, 20:343–350, 1957.

This article emphasizes the management of the total social situation of the patient in treatment. Family and staff interaction must be recognized as important, and must be understood and therapeutically and consistently managed in the treatment transaction.

FRANK, JEROME D. *Persuasion and Healing*. Baltimore, Johns Hopkins Press, 1961.

Dr. Frank emphasizes an approach to treatment which focuses on the common denominator of many psychotherapeutic endeavors. In our approach to the treatment transaction, we suggest the use of many resources which are not usually or clearly defined as treatment agencies. Under proper supervision utilization of many people and agencies in the community can extend the helping situation for the patient far beyond the medical model.

FREEMAN, HOWARD E., and SIMMONS, OZZIE G. *The Mental Patient Comes Home*. New York: John Wiley and Sons, Inc., 1963.

The authors report a study which surveys the problems for the community and the family when the patient leaves the hospital. The problems are not caused only by the patient's illness and by the society's and family's attitude toward mental illness, but also by the kind of "training" the patient receives in the hospital. In many hospital situations patients are "trained" to be "sick."

FROMM-REICHMANN, FRIEDA   Problems of Therapeutic Management in a Psychoanalytic Hospital. *Psychoanal. Quart.*, 16:325–356, 1947.
Dr. Fromm-Reichman was one of the leaders in the development of techniques of psychotherapy for the psychotic patient. Much of her talent and success was based on her personal qualities of genuine involvement and interest in her patients and an attitude of openness and hopefulness toward the favorable outcome of treatment of psychotic conditions.

GITELSON, MAXWELL   A Critique of Current Concepts of Psychosomatic Medicine. *Bull. Menninger Clin.*, 23:165–178, 1959.
This article reviews the development of the disease model from Robert Koch to Stewart Wolf.

GREENBLATT, MILTON, et al.   *The Patient and the Mental Hospital; Contributions of Research in the Science of Social Behavior.* Glencoe, Ill.: Free Press, 1957.
The mental hospital intervention in the treatment of psychosis can be of value. In our book we have described the indications for hospitalization, and also we have frequently reminded the reader of the many anti-therapeutic effects which mental hospitals produce.

HAMBURGER, WALTER H.   Emotional Aspects of Obesity. *Med. Clin. N. Amer.*, 35:483–499, 1951.
This paper describes the problem of obesity in relation to major mental illness. It demonstrates how overeating is a form of behavior which can be a symptom of an underlying psychosis. Interfering with the symptom of overeating (dieting) without considering the restitutive function of such a symptom may produce overt psychotic disorganization.

HOLLINGSHEAD, AUGUST B., and REDLICH, FREDRICK C.   *Social Class and Mental Illness.* New York: John Wiley & Sons, Inc., 1958.
This book has become an important classic of modern American psychiatric literature. It emphasizes the relationship of social class and attitudes toward symptoms, illness, and treatment.

HOCH, PAUL, and POLATIN, PHILLIP   Pseudoneurotic Forms of Schizophrenia. *Psychiat. Quart.*, 23:248–276, 1949.
This paper clarifies the very important concept that many schizophrenic patients seek help for neurotic symptoms. We have elaborated on this observation in our book. The failure of the therapist to recognize the underlying psychosis and his consequent treatment of the neurotic symptoms with expressive psychotherapeutic methods uniformly results in major psychotic disorganization.

KNIGHT, ROBERT P.   Psychotherapy of an Adolescent Catatonic Schizophrenia with Mutism. *Psychiatry*, 9:323–339, 1946.

This paper must be read for the music, not the words. Robert Knight writes about his experience with a very sick, very psychotic adolescent. He describes his treatment intervention using the terminology of psychoanalysis. However, he also describes in detail how he behaves with a patient and thus demonstrates the concept we have elaborated, namely, that what we do with a patient is what counts much more than what we say to the patient or how we describe the treatment transaction.

KNIGHT, ROBERT P.   Borderline States. *Bull. Menninger Clin.*, 17:1–12, 1953.

In this classic article an attempt is made to offer a guide to the clinician to help him to differentiate between the borderline psychotic patient and the neurotic patient.

KANNER, LEO   Irrelevant and Metaphorical Language in Early Infantile Autism. *Amer. J. Psychiat.*, 103:242–246, 1946.

The thesis of this article is to demonstrate by clinical illustration that all language, even the irrelevant language of the autistic child, can be understood within the context of the personal world of the patient.

MAZZANTI, VINCENT E., and BESSELL, HAROLD   Communication through Latent Language. *Amer. J. Psychother.*, 10:250–260, 1956.

Dr. Mazzanti, who has been one of our teachers, many years ago stimulated our interest in the treatment of the chronically ill schizophrenic patient. Many of his ideas became the starting point of our explorations for a theory and technique of treatment. In this paper, he and his co-author describe the concept of latent language which we have utilized in our book.

MENNINGER, KARL, ELLENBERGER, HENRI, PRUYSER, PAUL, and MAYMAN, MARTIN   The Unitary Concept of Mental Illness. *Bull. Menninger Clin.*, 22:4–12, 1958.

This article proposes a unitary concept of mental illness. It traces the history of classification of illness in psychiatry and concludes that there is essentially only one illness which patients manifest in varying degrees. Although we do not share this point of view and we do feel that the syndrome called schizophrenia is unique and has a clearly recognizable natural history, we do share Dr. Menninger's thesis of de-emphasizing nomenclature and of not using diagnostic labels pejoratively.

PARFITT, D. N.   The Neurology of Schizophrenia. *J. Ment. Sci.*, 102:671–718, 1956.

This paper looks at the symptoms of the schizophrenic patient as one would look at the symptoms of a neurological disease. Although, of course, at the present time there is no evidence for a neurological basis in the etiology of schizophrenia, we must remain open to such a possibility.

PARSONS, TALCOTT   Illness and the Role of the Physician, in Kluckhohn, C. and Murray, H., eds., *Personality in Nature, Society and Culture,* pp. 609–617. New York: Knopf, 1953.

The treatment response of the patient is determined by many factors other than the specific techniques of the therapist. Obviously, the patient comes with attitudes and expectations derived from his culture which will effect his response to the treatment intervention.

PARSONS, TALCOTT   Definitions of Health and Illness in the Light of American Values and Social Structure, in Jaco, E. G., ed., *Patients, Physicians and Illness.* Glencoe, Ill.: Free Press, 1958.

Therapeutic goals, as well as the concept of normality, are closely tied to the values of the culture. A physician coming from a different social class than a patient needs to be aware of the differences in values in order to be therapeutically effective.

POLATIN, PHILLIP, and HOCH, PAUL   Diagnostic Evaluation of Early Schizophrenia. *J. Nerv. Ment. Dis.,* 105:221–230, 1947.

A list of symptoms which should make the physician suspicious of the possibility of the presence of schizophrenia in a patient is given in this article.

RUESCH, JURGEN, BRODSKY, CARROLL, and FISCHER, AMES   The Acute Nervous Breakdown. *Arch. Gen. Psychiat.,* 8:197–207, 1963.

An approach to the understanding and treatment of the patient with an acute psychotic disorganization is presented.

SECHEHAYE, MARGUERITE ALBERT   *Reality Lost and Regained; Autobiography of a Schizophrenic Girl;* with analytical interpretation. Rubin-Rabson, Grace (trans.), New York: Grune and Stratton, 1951, pt. I, p. 1–106.

Detailed subjective descriptions of the patient suffering from a schizophrenic illness, such as the one given here, are of great value to all therapists dealing with such patients. An understanding of the patient's feelings will lead to a clearer recognition of the meaning of symptoms and of the requirements for therapy.

STANTON, ALFRED H., and SCHWARTZ, MORRIS S.   *The Mental Hospital.* New York: Basic Books, 1954.

This book became a classic in the exploration of the psychological and social transactions in the hospital situation. It pioneered in the evaluation of the treatment transaction within the hospital.

szasz, thomas   The Myth of Mental Illness. *American Psychologist,* 15:113–118, 1960.

In this article questions are raised as to the validity of the medical model in mental illness. Misbehavior which is the manifestation of a postulated underlying disease process does not easily fit into the conceptualization of symptoms and disease. How then can we approach mental illness? Dr. Szasz gives no answer to this, but he stimulates the reader to be critical of the naïve application of the medical model in the field of mental illness.

zilboorg, gregory   Ambulatory Schizophrenias. *Psychiatry,* 4:149–155, 1941.

Ambulatory schizophrenia, another term for the patient who is not overtly psychotic, but who is schizophrenic and requires treatment, is described in this article. The recognition of such patients is of the utmost importance, so that they can be appropriately treated by such methods as outlined in our book.

Index